FLY FIS

BY

J. R. HARTLEY

Memories of Angling Days

ILLUSTRATED BY
PATRICK BENSON

Fly Fishing: Memories of Angling Days

by J. R. Hartley

Fly Fishing: Memories of Angling Days

by J. R. Hartley

Illustrated by Patrick Benson

First published in 1991

Copyright © 1991 by J. R. Hartley

First published 1991
Reprinted 1991 (three times)

A catalogue record for this book is available
upon request from the British Library

This Printing in June, 2015 by Ishi Press in New York and Tokyo with a new introduction by Sam Sloan

Copyright © 2015 by Sam Sloan

ISBN 4-87187-689-6
978-4-87187-689-6

Ishi Press International
1664 Davidson Avenue, Suite 1B
Bronx NY 10453-7877
USA
1-917-659-3397
samhsloan@gmail.com
Printed in the United States of America

Introduction by Sam Sloan

Fly Fishing: Memories of Angling Days
by J. R. Hartley
Introduction by Sam Sloan

Fly Fishing is a fake book. Right now you are probably asking yourself, "how could a book be fake" especially as you are holding it in your hands.

Funny story about this. **Fly Fishing by J. R. Hartley** was a fake non-existent book used as a prop in a series of TV advertisements in England for the Yellow Pages of the telephone company. After the ad was taken off the air, somebody decided to make a real book by that name. It has no author listed, as J. R. Hartley was a fake person.

In the ad, an elderly man seen on the back cover here is looking for a certain book. He wanders from store to store but none of the stores have this book.

His daughter asks him what he is looking for and when he answers, she tells him to look in the Yellow Pages.

The man looks in the yellow pages and immediately finds a store that has the book. The name of the book is "Fly Fishing by J. R. Hartley".

This ad ran on TV in England for years. It became the punch line for a joke. J. R. Hartley's best-known catch to date is not a fish but the public imagination. Here are his elusive fishing recollections told in a series of sometimes vividly comic chronological cameos, ranging period and location from York school days in the early 1930s through memorable outings on stream, spate river and loch to startling conclusion half a lifetime later on a Scottish summer night.

Introduction by Sam Sloan

Complimented by his protege Patrick Benson's evocative illustrations and with his anglers expertise lightly threaded throughout, J. R.'s story will touch every fly fisherman's experience. But it is book too that will appeal to everyone even those who have never held a rod, for the engaging point that emerges of the ultimate reluctant hero.

In Britain years back, there was an advert for a telephone directory, and an old man kept going from store to store looking for a book, the title of which was Fly Fishing, by J.R. Hartley. He didn't have any luck finding the book, so his daughter said to try the telephone to do the work. He found a book via the telephone, when he asked the person to keep the book on hold, he was asked his name. His name... J.R. Hartley.

This presents an interesting legal issue. It often happens that the characters in a movie or a TV show are shown discussing a book. Almost invariably there is no real book by that name. The name of the book is a mere plot device for events that take place later in the movie.

In the book and movies "The Great Gatsby", this happens. In The Great Gatsby they discuss a book supposedly by Goddard. According to the leading character in the movie, the White race is superior to all other races and we were born to rule, so we have the obligation to keep the other races down.

Actually, there is no such book by Henry H. Goddard, although he wrote several books. Instead, such a book was written by Lothrop Stoddard. He wrote "The Rising Tide of Color Against White World-Supremacy". Note the similarity in the last names of the authors.

Introduction by Sam Sloan

What we can do is go around looking for movies where part if the plot involves discussing a book. When it is established that no such book exists, we write and publish the book!!! I can see nothing legally wrong with this.

What about the case where an actor adopts the name and personality of another living person? When Tina Fey started doing imitations of Vice-Presidential Candidate Sarah Palin, her imitations were so good that nobody, not even close friends of Sarah Palin, could tell whether Tina Fey was playing her or the real Sarah Palin was there.

Fly Fishing Memories of Angling Days seems to be the biography of a real person. It contains names of people and places where they lived. There is no hint within the book that these stories are fake. One of the characters in the book is Jock McBain. There are several people in the world with that name. Is one of them being depicted in this book?

The question is whether I can get into trouble for reprinting this book. This book is ranked as number 40 on the Bookfinder dot com annual list of most sought for books that are out of print. This book has been out of print since 1993. Thus, it has not been available for 22 years. Under copyright law, the copyright belongs to the author. We know that the author listed here, JR Hartley, is a fake, no-existent person. There must be a real author, but we do not know who it is.

If the real author wants to claim that I have violated his rights to this book, he will have to admit that J. R. Hartley is a fake non-existent person, that this biography is a fraud and that he wrote it. How will he prove this? I think it cannot be proven.

Introduction by Sam Sloan

This question often comes up with authors who write under pseudonyms. I have discovered many cases of authors who wrote under pseudonyms but nobody has suspected it. When I reprint a book I always include a brief biography of the author so I look him up to see if he is still alive and, if he is dead, when and where he died, where he is buried and if he left a wife or children.

In doing this, I have discovered two cases of famous authors who wrote more than thirty books each and who are known to be dead but there is no official record of their deaths. In the USA, all people who die after about 1963 are listed in the Social Security Death Index, assuming they had a social security number which almost everybody has nowadays. If the name of a deceased author cannot be found in the social security death index, that tends to indicate that the person wrote under a pseudonym.

Many famous authors have written under a pseudonym. I think this happens more often in England than in the USA. In many cases, their real name is now known. For example, **Lewis Carroll**, the famous author of *Alice's Adventures in Wonderland,* was actually **Charles Lutwidge Dodgson**. One can easily imagine reasons why he did not write under his real name. The Queen of Hearts was often shouting "Off With His Head". The Queen of Hearts clearly resembled Queen Victoria, who was in power at the time. The husband of Queen Victoria, Prince Albert, clearly resembled the King of Hearts. Whether the real Queen Victoria had the power to have a man's head chopped off whenever she felt the inclination to do so is not known today.

Dodgson must have feared that he would be arrested upon the publication of this book. It is also now known that

Dodgson was interested in little girls. He may have feared the police for that reason as well.

I have tried searching the names, dates, places, text and events described in **Fly Fishing: Memories of Angling Days** to find the original author and the reason for which it was written. I have come up with nothing. The real author was clearly a talented writer. The lack of public curiosity as to the identity of the true author of this work tells me that somebody must know. Perhaps if I were English rather than American the answer to this riddle would be apparent. However, because I could not solve it and could not find out the answer, I have decided to write this introduction to reprint it.

Sam Sloan
Novato, California
USA
June 24, 2015

Contents

Acknowledgements

My grateful thanks are due to my searchmates, Yellow Pages; to my publisher Roderick Bloomfield, for revitalising the quest; to Peter Lapsley, for appraising these memoirs with his expert angler's eye; and to Michael Russell, for setting them down.

J.R.H.

An Echo from the Past

Although we had come to live in Hampshire, where my father practised as a country doctor, our roots were in the North. When I was thirteen therefore, in an impractical concession to old loyalties, I was sent to school at Arborleigh, high in the Yorkshire North Riding. The country at least was familiar; I had stayed often at my grandparents' sheltered stone house up in Loderdale, and it was on the North Yorkshire rain-fed rivers that I learnt my wet fly craft. My grandfather, who had been vicar of Copsall Bridge, was held locally in great affection. He was a dear man, one of the old breed of clergyman-naturalists, much more interested in the grey wagtail than the Pentateuch, mild-mannered yet with the capacity to surprise – my aunt, for instance, told me he had made her attend all children's parties dressed as Hereward the Wake. His wife, my father's mother, I think adored him, though she conducted her married life much as she played the 'cello, with a look of serenity but sparing on the *vibrato*.

My fishing mentor, at my grandfather's instigation, was Jock McBain, landlord of the Hero of Inkerman in Copsall Bridge and the most commanding fisherman into a wind I ever saw. He had been head gillie on a grand estate in Scotland but came south after falling out with his employer. He led us to suppose that he was the injured party, but the very idea of inflicting injury on Jock McBain seemed so improbable that I should like to have heard the employer's version of the story. Jock would have rejected it of course, because concession of any kind was not in his makeup. He regarded his exile merely as an unwelcome change of scenery, his Scottishness uncompromised as the slow broad manner of the dales lapped unavailingly against it. He even had the sign outside his public house repainted to put the Hero in a kilt.

Mostly we fished the River Loder, where it potters down between the villages that punctuate the upper dale. It could shrink in summer to a rusty trickle in the upper reaches; then, with the onset of the rain, swell quickly to a striding torrent that would have the village boys out worming. We, more decorously, would wait a few more hours until the water began to settle and we could look forward to a bag of small strong brownies caught on Red or Orange Partridge, Poult Bloa or Snipe and Purple. Not perhaps the game for your chalk stream purist, but ideal at an age when patience expects to be rewarded. Whatever they may say about travelling hopefully having the edge on arriving, there is much to be said for being able to make the comparison. Worth remembering if you're teaching young people to fish with the fly. I liked fishing then because I had caught fish. That, when you're starting, is why you continue. At the heart of it all is the feel of the fish on the line.

There was however the problem of taking life. Seeing grouse shot up on the moors distressed and rather disgusted me. Should I be trying to kill things too? I was reassured to find that the Bible no less, unless I was misunderstanding something, seemed to be giving us the nod.

I consulted my grandfather. 'Jesus was keen on fishing, wasn't he?' I inquired, trying to keep the optimism out of my voice.

'The disciples were fishers of men,' he replied.

It was said most reassuringly and, knowing my grandfather, I've no doubt that was his intention. Still, it seemed an odd notion that anyone as obviously discriminating as a disciple should want to catch the Bible lands' equivalent of the Harker brothers or the Ulsterman with the moose jaw who drove Mr Vellacott's grocery van.

'So Jesus doesn't mind us hurting his things?'

'It isn't like that,' my grandfather said.

He didn't go on to explain what it was like. But for some time the problem with my conscience receded.

My father bought me an eight-foot-six split-cane rod from a retired major in Wotton-under-Edge. I have it still, its tip well out of true from unnumbered tugs of war with rocks and overhanging branches, and spliced just below the middle after an involvement with the front wheel of my bicycle. I absorbed from Jock McBain the general principles of casting – not to hold the rod too tight, not to take the point back beyond twelve o'clock, and so on – and he left me, sensibly, to refine it on my own. I got used to the hook in the back of my neck, the whirr of the flying tangle and the cast gyrating round my outstretched hand, always a fraction out of reach. My reel came off, my rod came in two, my waders filled with water, a horse trod on my lunch. I almost gave up fishing a score of times, and a score of times the line rifled out precisely where I was aiming and a quick-turning trout made me a fisherman again.

Fishing memories mature into exaggeration, but there is an accumulation of experience that begins to stand one in good stead. There are no certainties about what will happen and what will not, but there are broad patterns of predictability (mostly about what will not). You begin to be able to appraise a stretch of water, to sense where the fish will be. On wet fly water this is essential, because, unlike on dry fly water, the fish is not normally giving his position away. The Loder was a good training ground for a lifetime's fishing with the fly, because after the first seasons of scrambling the line away downstream, Jock showed me how to proceed the other way, using a short line to cast upstream with just a tail fly and a single dropper. You raise your hand to keep the line taut, casting very frequently, letting the flies travel back no more than three yards or so towards you. Strike at the slightest check, because that is the only indication you will have in rough water that the fish is taking.

There were a few slow runs on the Loder, with back-eddies where a rill joined the main stream. Good fish lay there and, particularly towards the end of the season, Jock would tempt them with a dry fly. I was watching him one day when he pointed to a rising fish under the opposite bank, passed me his rod and nodded for me to try my luck. My cast was straight enough but a little too far. The fly checked on an overhanging dock leaf, then, ever so gently, slipped down to settle on the water. I knew somehow in that breathless moment that here was my first fish on the dry fly. He took, a ten-inch trout, and I was ready for him.

The fisherman's worst tribulations in my experience are a mischievous wind and Scottish midges – though by some providential dispensation the two tend not to hunt in pairs. The midge, unlike the heftier and less subtle 'cleg', who regards you simply as an outsize Bloody Mary, relies on numbers and an insidious approach, goading you to a frenzy of irritation. Once, fishing on a still night for sea trout on the west coast of Scotland, I was reduced almost literally to tears. I had smeared my face with generous defences of fly-repellent but left the backs of my hands quite unprotected. Be warned.

The wind brings other lessons. It teaches you not to 'press' when casting into it, to rely on control and less ambitious distances; and that in turn teaches another valuable lesson. There is a temptation in the early stages of your fly-fishing career to cast too far. To begin with, there is something robust about it, a satisfying way of showing off. But then think of all the fish you've hooked surprisingly close to you on a well-presented fly and you'll begin to appreciate how much good water you've wasted by casting unnecessarily long. In Yorkshire, on the Loder or the Wharfe, with a stiff wind blowing downstream, I would cast as if I were throwing the javelin, with a sodden line putting down every fish between me and the cast. My grandfather thought it a wonderful display, but Jock McBain was unimpressed. He made me turn and practise casting into the wind. It was less like throwing the javelin, more like throwing a dart.

Arborleigh is near the head of Dommettdale, which runs west to east to join Loderdale at Copsall Bridge. The school buildings cluster in a broad bulge of the dale before the road climbs abruptly to high open moorland and a view that takes some minutes to digest. There is a lay-by there these days, where people stop their cars and wonder as they eat their sausage rolls whether those distant outlines could be the Lakeland peaks. Gym shoes squelching, we would toil up there on rainy afternoons, pausing, hands on hips, to ease the stitch before starting downwards on the friendlier return.

Down dale, not two miles from Copsall Bridge, where the Dommett threads between steep fells with only the single-track road to keep it company, there is a famous echo. The farmers, weaving home at night, would stop to test it with jocular obscenities that reverberated grossly up and down the dale in an affront to Nature's dignity that would have horrified poor Wordsworth. We knew the place, more soberly, as the turning point in a dreadful ritual called the Echo Run, to which the juniors were subjected in each of the two winter terms. Restricted to the single shout of our own surnames, we would be checked there by a waiting master before turning to begin the uphill second half.

My best friend at Arborleigh was Easby-Norris, who sprang to wider fame one field day by shooting Regimental Sergeant-

Major Harmsworth with a pencil during our platoon attack. My parents urged me on the strength of this to invite him in the holidays, which I did, but then most gracelessly – for ours was a happy family life – I began to have misgivings in case it should be discovered and reported back to school that we were rough-edged or, in ways I'd not suspected, not quite *comme il faut.* My father didn't help in this regard by getting out his stethoscope at tea to listen to my mother's simnel cake – I couldn't believe that was how the Easby-Norrises behaved – but Easby-Norris laughed his head off and confided to me afterwards that he thought my people were great fun.

I couldn't in honesty have returned the compliment when I was invited back to High Wood, the house that Colonel Easby-Norris had renamed to remind him of the Somme. It stood in an acre of respectability in a Surrey village not far from the Devil's Punch Bowl, which I nervously imagined would be full of adders and so declined repeated suggestions that we should go there for a picnic. The houseproud Mrs Easby-Norris was meticulously tidy with a mania for dainty sandwiches, and was always asking Easby-Norris, in my presence, what I would like to do. Colonel Easby-Norris was briskly military. He would erode your confidence with interrogatory sentences, then suddenly break off in mid-conversation to give you the most unnerving glare. He had won two Military Crosses on the Western Front and was not at all the sort of customer you'd want in the opposing sector.

Meanwhile my career progressed at Arborleigh. I was found to have a talent for Latin and leg-break bowling, a comprehensive enough portfolio to ingratiate me with the majority of the staff, though because of my association with Easby-Norris not even a sudden reincarnation as Lord Kitchener would have redeemed me in the eyes of Regimental Sergeant-Major Harmsworth. I had resolved, to the satisfaction of my conscience, the difference between morality and school rules, which when I had first arrived I had mistakenly supposed to be the same. So if I got into trouble, I knew it would be something on which I could defend myself to my parents and that they would understand. This did not make me rash or lawless but I admit it kept in the back of my mind the possibility of a discreet visit to my grandparents or even Jock McBain. But one had to be careful. The headmaster, 'Tilter' Lemoine, had lost part of his right leg at the Battle of Jutland, shattered by a shell that had been fired from over the horizon, to become, improbably, a metaphor for retribution should we venture out of bounds.

At the end of my third summer term a party of us went to the Loderdale Show. Exams were over and there was scarcely a week to go before the holidays. Tilter thought it might be a gesture to local good relations if some senior boys attended, so we were presented with a list of dos and don'ts and threatened as to what might happen if we failed to report back to the charabancs at half past four. Then we were issued with a small amount of spending money (charged to our parents' bills), inspected for tidinesss and counted aboard the waiting transport. It was a sparkling day and our morale was high. My housemaster, however, Mr Oglethorpe, who was in charge of our bus, was evidently not happy to be included in the outing. He was wearing a most inappropriate suit of mulligatawny Harris tweed, which from the way he was flicking himself about seemed to be tickling everything except his fancy. He rebuked us for cheering when our driver forced an open car to reverse about three hundred yards to allow us room to pass; and he had shown no signs of becoming infected with the air of carnival by the time the bus boiled over and we came to rest.

There was no more than a mile to walk but we soon built up a substantial lead on Mr Oglethorpe as, clutching our packed lunches, we made our way towards the entrance of the show. He was waving his arms about at something but we adjudged him out of range and chose to assume it was only a rhetorical gesture about the thickness of his suit. Inside the ground the bookmakers were chalking up their odds about the outcome of the fell race. The sheepdog trials were already under way; in various tents the more staid competitive events were laid out for inspection. For me of course the star attraction, billed for 2.15, was the casting demonstration by Jock McBain.

I went to find him. He greeted me warmly, rather too warmly, for I could see he was quite drunk. I thought we might be in for an embarrassing fiasco, but his casting, when the moment came, was quite impeccable. He wielded an eighteen-foot two-hander with exemplary control and the crowd gave him a well-deserved ovation. Unfortunately there were some bystanders, less responsible than the rest, who pressed him then to more refreshments and so precipitated the sorry incident that followed.

I was standing with my grandparents when we saw Jock walk unsteadily out into the field with his rod and, egged on by a section of the crowd, begin to make false casts in the direction of a local farmer who was participating in the sheepdog trials. The man was already having a frustrating afternoon. For all his shouts and whistles, his collie seemed bent on misinterpreting his instructions and had overpowered a lone sheep on one of the tables in the tea tent. You expect some disappointments in a life lived close to the land, but not, in the middle of a totally ig-nominious public performance by your best dog, to be struck in the back by a number 4 Thunder and Lightning coming out of nowhere with the power of a diving gannet.

It was when Jock, to a crescendo of cheering, began to reel in the struggling farmer that Major Salkeld, one of the stewards, came up to restore order. He wrested Jock's rod away from him and ordered him to leave the field. This Jock angrily declined to do and broke in half the Major's ram's horn crook, brandishing the pieces like some crazed evangelist until he was knocked out by Major Salkeld's wife, a woman with the physique of Primo Carnera and the social graces of an avalanche who was known in Yorkshire society as the Lonsdale Belter.

He came round soon enough and, after some ministrations by the doctor, was helped into my grandfather's car and driven back to his public house to rest. The Hero of Inkerman was definitely among the don'ts of our afternoon's instructions and even Easby-Norris thought it unwise to risk a visit there with Mr Oglethorpe hanging around us tut-tutting about the evils of drink and looking extremely uncomfortable, I was glad to see, in his mulligatawny suit. So our trip to Loderdale Show took on a note of anti-climax, only momentarily relieved when the Lonsdale Belter broke the Great Strength Rings the Bell machine. We reported to the charabanc park with spirits subdued and travelled back to school in almost total silence.

Easby-Norris and I were due that evening to act as stage hands in the school play. It was a surprise therefore when he appeared in my room soon after 7.15 carrying two Homburg hats and two beards. Plans were altered, he announced. He had arranged for two boys to replace us at the play and he and I, disguised as rabbis, were going in to Copsall Bridge on Mr Oglethorpe's motor bicycle, which Easby-Norris had established was presently in an unlocked shed behind the house.

I hardly knew what to say. What if my grandfather were taking a constitutional up towards the echo and, lowering his binoculars from the outline of a curlew on the fell, should happen to see his grandson sail past as a rabbi? There were connotations here that might considerably unsettle him. Easby-Norris thought this fussy stuff. He lobbed a hat and beard towards me, enjoined me not to forget my overcoat and said he'd meet me round the bend below the house in seven minutes' time.

With the gravest misgivings I hurried down to the road and turned left. As soon as I was out of sight of the school buildings I put on my disguise. Almost at once I heard the sound of an approaching motor cycle and there was Easby-Norris, good as his word, looking pleasantly ridiculous in beard and hat.

The ride itself was exhilarating; there was an illicit bouquet to that summer evening air I shall not easily forget. We swept past the echo with a double honk on the klaxon that the fellside good-humouredly acknowledged. A party of walkers returning down the dale scrambled into single file to let us pass. Then we were up to the main road and bowling into Copsall Bridge.

Jock McBain came to the back door rather warily in answer to our knocking, but visibly cheered up when we removed our beards and Homburg hats. We laughed, over glasses of cider, about the afternoon's mishaps – from which he seemed none the worse – and he told me about the one and a half pounder he'd had last Wednesday from the top of Roddam's Pool. His obvious approval of our exploit flattered us, though it was hardly for me to take much of the credit. The fact was that Easby-Norris had exceptional spirit and organisational panache. He would have been the man to win the war but he turned out to have something wrong with his knees and became an actuary instead.

As we were preparing to leave, Jock challenged me, apparently on impulse, to a round of what we called 'Alternates'. It was a private fishing game we played, where you took alternate casts with the same rod and moved down river until one or other caught a fish. We'd start, he said, just below the echo. He'd take his van and drop me off at school. Easby-Norris could lead the way.

I suppose Jock must have mistrusted Easby-Norris's ability to carry me safely back to Arborleigh; and as we accelerated up the High Street, with Easby-Norris out in front, we could detect a certain insouciance about his control of the machine. Perhaps it was the cider, but as we turned up the Dommett-dale road he began to weave from side to side, crouched in an exaggerated racing position and singing for all he was worth. An inexperienced pillion passenger might not have stayed the course.

Just before the echo Easby-Norris pulled into the side and turned, laughing, to watch us draw up on the verge behind him. His engine was still running and as Jock and I got out to walk down towards the water with our rod, he called out something and moved off up the road. We heard him stop round the bend at the echo, and as Jock was making his first cast the cry of 'Tilter, Tilter' carried down the dale towards us. Easby-Norris was being most unwise.

I won our competition, fifth cast, in the second pool. I let the flies run down the rough water and straighten out in a deeper race between two rocks. A little brown trout took my tail Black Spider and I wound him in; then, holding him firmly with thumb and forefinger over his gills, I detached the hook, set him level in the water and let him go. Jock watched me approvingly and conceded defeat. We walked back to the van.

There was no sign of Easby-Norris as we passed the echo and began the gradual climb up towards the school. He seemed to have got safely back; at least no parts of Mr Oglethorpe's motor cycle nor of its temporary partner were visible on the road. When we reached the entrance to the house we looked round carefully to make sure the coast was clear. I blurted out my thanks and slunk in, my disguise in a bundle under my arm. It was still a few minutes before late lockup.

The news was terrible. It transpired that Matron, chancing to look out of the sick room window, had seen Easby-Norris making off with Mr Oglethorpe's machine. She had alerted the authorities and an intercepting party had set off in pursuit. When Easby-Norris stopped to shout the headmaster's name at the echo, Regimental Sergeant-Major Harmsworth and a policeman appeared suddenly from behind the wall. Easby-Norris was escorted to the police van parked further up the road. After a pungent reunion with Mr Oglethorpe, he was sent to the headmaster. Tilter had indicated his shattered leg, and recalled the shell that came over the Jutland horizon. RSM Harmsworth's unexpected appearance at the echo, he said, was not without its parallels. Rules were not made for fun. Easby-Norris was expelled.

I was distraught. No, Easby-Norris said gamely, there was no point in incurring unnecessary casualties. I was not suspected and he had said all along that he was the only one involved.

They had reckoned of course without Colonel Easby-Norris. I was standing watching our luggage being loaded on to the railway dray when a dark-brown four-cylinder Riley drew up and the colonel got out wearing a bowler hat and a dark-brown two-cylinder bird's-eye suit. I retreated behind the lea of a pile of trunks but he'd already seen me.

'Hiding, Hartley?'

'No, sir, just checking labels.'

He looked at me with distaste and expressed the hope that the keys were irredeemably lost to whichever trunk contained his son. Then he pulled an envelope out of his pocket.

'I've had a preposterous letter from that jumped up one-legged powder monkey who imagines he's some sort of headmaster.'

This, if unfair, was encouragingly assertive. Would there be a chance, I asked the colonel, of seeing Mr Lemoine and asking him to reconsider his decision?

'I should think there bloody well would.'

My spirits began to rise. I couldn't see Tilter going the distance with the colonel in this mood. I accompanied him silently to the private side, where Mr Oglethorpe appeared, bobbing like a feeding wader.

Easby-Norris came back as usual on the first day of next term, to the cheerful astonishment of the school. His father, he said, had been to see the headmaster and there'd been a change of plan.

2

Rod and Gown

In the autumn of 1936 I went up to Oxford. I had been awarded an exhibition to a minor college, which at Arborleigh brought out the bunting; but the transition from the small pond to the large was difficult. From having been the pride of the creel, I was suddenly the one you had to put back. I was socially ungilded, academically just about competent, with a moderate facility for the classics. But I was inclined to work. A sympathetic tutor in those first terms would have transformed my university career. Instead I was allotted a curdled chain-smoking poseur called Dr Pollard, known as 'Puffer' for his habit with the weed.

He was by now as much of a college institution as the chef's Lancashire hotpot or the Master's dog, which had a good deal in common except that one of them (the hotpot) moved. Extending the mythology about Puffer had become an art form of its own. He had been, it must be said, an appreciable scholar in his day but by the time I came under his supervision the spring had gone out of his intellectual step, although he couldn't have been much over fifty. He seemed more interested in projecting himself as a university 'card', but because he had about as much charm as a burst pipe his affectations were neither endearing nor amusingly provocative. He was the Square Peg in the Round Table. Or was it the Low Peg in the High Table?

One of his more enjoyable misfires concerned the mynah bird that he bought in a local pet shop. He had announced to everyone that he was going to teach it to recite the first few books of the *Iliad*, but the bird was obviously quite a bit older than the shopkeeper had suggested and had lost its appetite for the classics. Puffer spent weeks leaning into its face enunciating Greek hexameters, but the only phrase the creature was ever heard to utter – though admittedly very frequently – was 'Blackburn Rovers'.

The field of human vision, even if your eyes are as close together as Puffer's, is such that there is no need to move your head up and down when taking in the appearance of someone who is no more than a couple of yards away. To do so, unless you have a professional interest in turnout like a sergeant-major or a tailor, is to make an evaluative statement. Puffer did it every time, with a look of critical superiority on his face that was intended to make you feel a poorly turned out worm. He himself dressed rather expensively, with good suits as often as not accentuated by brown and white co-respondent's shoes, which seemed in his case the ultimate in wishful thinking. His voice was reedy and querulous, he wore gloves and a cape, and he sniffed.

Our tutorials took place in his cluttered rooms in Holywell, which he shared with the mynah bird and a favourite cat. Everything reeked of nicotine. Among the furnishings and bric-a-brac there was a signed photograph of Mae West. One couldn't imagine two more disparate components in the cocktail of life than Puffer and Mae. Puffer never offered an explanation of the photograph, and just in case he was waiting for us to ask, we never did. The mystery remained unsolved. Not that Puffer's explanation would necessarily have been the truth. Most likely the photograph was a studio handout that he had acquired in a second-hand shop. I wasn't going to show

I cared any more than he cared about the work I brought him, which he glanced through rapidly to see if it contained anything over which he could be dismissive or sarcastic. His termly reports were wittily destructive. None of this had anything to do with good teaching, which is surely in part about encouragement. That first year with Puffer bludgeoned my morale.

Then, with my first set of examinations approaching, I was taken quite severely ill. It was diagnosed variously as glandular fever, encephalitis and 'nothing much', and the neurological expertise that was invoked on my behalf seemed rather contradictory. I was paraded before various specialists who looked at me with interest, and in some cases curiosity. I came away from their consultancy with the suspicion that it had been more for their benefit than mine. Meanwhile I missed a term.

I was back in Oxford in the summer of 1938, still fragile but in a happier frame of mind. I had exchanged the smoky domains of Puffer Pollard for the sunny disarray of Spencer Brandt. Apart from being an idiosyncratic but invigorating teacher, Spencer was a dedicated angler. Our tutorials became more and more encroached upon by talk of fishing, until he would glance guiltily at his watch and switch to his professional duties with a grimace of self-reproach. We got on well. He was a man of broad interests, with a capacity to entertain and an uncontrived intimacy that made you feel not just that he was a don being nice to you but that he was actually your friend.

Two fly-fishing enthusiasts had also come up to the college at the beginning of my second year – Henry Fisk and Lawrence Wilkes. They were up for three years and I for four, so our prospects marched together and we settled into an easy rapport that sustained the three of us as lifelong friends. I introduced them to Spencer Brandt and soon we were all making fly-fishing expeditions together to the Gloucestershire Coln.

Spencer arranged everything and generously paid, usually insisting on indulgent lunches at the Bull Hotel at Fairford after we had taken our chances with the morning rise. He drove us down in his old open Lagonda which he spurred along the highway without too much concern for other traffic, but the sheer ramming power of the bonnet in front of you and the thrust of the wind in your face somehow commuted the risk into enjoyable adventure.

The Coln is a limestone river – though you might suppose it a classic chalk stream – flowing through clean, rich Cotswold country. There is a feeling of no-nonsense prosperity about the stone-built manor houses set in estates marked out by drystone walls, where one suspects that even the horses bank with Coutts. The soft sameness of the stone gives a cohesion to the villages, the warm golden-grey of the steeply pitched tiled roofs only slightly darker than their supporting walls. All the English trees are here, oaks and ashes, and great stands of beech, mature and leisurely compared to the hastier imported larch and spruce.

The river was ten to fifteen yards wide where we fished, three to five feet deep, flowing sinuously over beds of water crowfoot and water milfoil. In good conditions it would be gin clear, with occasional dark pools tucked in beneath overhanging willows. From a selfish point of view, it was a snag that there was a public right of way along the bank. All too often an uncomprehending walker would stop to engage us in well-meant discussion after the inevitable greeting, thrown from twenty yards, of 'Any luck?' Spencer, though he was a courteous man, could not resist responding 'Up till now.'

We fished upstream dry fly from the bank – to rising fish – and by September the vegetation would be allowed to grow to a height of three to four feet to provide the angler cover. Lawrence and I went down with Spencer right at the end of the season in September 1938. We had returned to Oxford early from the Long Vacation to catch up on some reading and to have one last day at Fairford on the Coln. There were purple-crowned patches of huge high thistles in the meadows and mushrooms for the taking. For flies we matched the Medium Olive with the artificial Greenwell's Glory (size 14-16), the Medium Olive Spinner with Lunn's Particular, the Blue-Winged Olive with Orange Quill, and the Sherry Spinner and the sedge-fly Caperer with artificials of that name. There was a chill in the dusk, a slight melancholy in the thought of another season slipped away, and longer silences than usual coming back to Oxford in the car.

Meanwhile we watched the drift to war. There was a general awareness that our turn was coming, but there was anticipation as well as foreboding in the talk of active service. We were buoyed by class and confidence to believe that Britain finally taught squirts like Hitler a lesson; moral superiority was more than a position, it presupposed a result. The state of our defences might be less than wonderful (how much less we would have been appalled to know) but there was always luck or God – and both were English.

By the time we entered our last year at Oxford, the predictions had become certainty and war had been declared. Those of us who were staying for a final year were more than conscious of the loss of vitality in the place; yet through the Phoney War there was still a surprising degree of normality. We hadn't all been bombed to pieces, the trains still ran, you could still eat well in the right restaurant. Come June 1940, you could even persuade yourself in an Alice in Wonderland sort of way that the retrieval of so many fighting men from Dunkirk had turned the French disasters into victory.

With final examinations over, we decided to have a last day together on the Coln. Spencer had some petrol for the Lagonda and we set off for Coln St Aldwyn on a fine summer morning. In France, at Compiegne, Hitler was imposing his terms of surrender in a vengeful reversal of November 1918.

The previous week Churchill had rallied us with his 'finest hour' speech in the House of Commons; Mussolini had just brought Italy into the war. The head porter told me that the Duce's timing was 'typical of the ice creamers' and did I know that the King was practising revolver shooting in the gardens of Buckingham Palace? I said no, I hadn't heard that but I'd feel a lot safer now taking a day's fishing on the Coln.

We were down by the river soon after eleven and disposed ourselves up and down the bank. By one o'clock Henry, Lawrence and I had six fish between us, one of them – Lawrence's – all but three pounds. Only Spencer had missed out and he patrolled between us, checking which flies had been successful, puzzled at the imbalance of our fortunes and finally calling a halt for lunch to stop the rot. We were out of range of the Bull at Fairford today, above Coln St Aldwyn, near Hatherop, so we settled back in the grass under hot sunshine to have our picnic. Spencer had acquired three good bottles of white burgundy from the college cellar, and now ingeniously claimed that immersing them in his beat of the river to keep them cool had scared away the trout.

It was a precious day. We knew there couldn't be so many more together before we were carried away on the flood of the uncertain future. Henry and Lawrence would be in khaki in a matter of weeks. I was not so sure; there were still some question marks about my health. What would Regimental Sergeant-Major Harmsworth be thinking now, having to depend on the likes of Easby-Norris and myself? We all seemed most unlikely heroes. Would we manage what was expected of us? It helped to talk about it with someone like Spencer who was articulate and understanding. He had been an unlikely soldier too, yet had found reserves to acquit himself respectably in some fearsome fighting on the Western Front. He knew about the strengths of companionship in danger, the mental attitudes required to cope with inactivity, the tricks of survival, the spectre of a pointless death. From the survivor's side of a horrific war he could look at things more analytically. He thought that bravery in isolation demanded more special qualities than bravery 'in the herd'; you could probably only get a company of men to run over a cliff in step. Henry replied laconically that he was trying to get into a regiment where there was an officer with the sense to tell them not to.

We laughed and talked, cocooned in the country stillness and the brightness of the afternoon. Then gradually I felt an odd disquiet that all this perfection could only be a final treat. I had a premonition that I was going to lose my friends. I watched Lawrence and Henry walk off down the field to fish. They were no more than fifty yards away, conversing together with rods stretched back on their shoulders, when a cloud covered the sun and the shadow raced across the grass between us. They turned to look up in surprise as it came upon them from behind. Spencer and I, so close, were still in sunshine. The shadow seemed symbolically to isolate our separate fortunes, to confirm my private fears. It was an omen. I looked at Spencer, wondering if he had seen it too. He was lying back in the sun, his eyes were closed.

I gathered up the picnic things and took them over to the car. When I got back Spencer was crouched by the river bank, alert now, waiting for any sign of a fish. Nothing moved. The breeze had dropped completely.

'What's the matter?' he asked, without looking up.

'I had a curious experience,' I said, feeling suddenly foolish; but I told him what had happened. 'Do you think it was telling me something?'

'No, I think you were telling it something. It's just what's on your mind. Lawrence and Henry have to join up and you're worried that they'll have a more dangerous time of it than you. That's probably true. It's not some paranormal tip-off.'

He was right of course. But that image, for all my rationalising, stayed with me as a presentiment, to trouble me for years to come.

Spencer thought we must forgo the evening rise to be back in Oxford by the blackout. We should have supper with him, and he'd cook our fish. Reluctant though we were to tear ourselves away, the prospect of Spencer's driving with the hooded headlights won the day. Besides, the fish were being very wary. I had one brown trout on an Orange Quill but he disposed of me in the weeds. Then, shortly before we packed up, there was a shout of triumph from Spencer further up the river and he caught a two pound grayling. The grayling season had only just begun and they are at their poorest when trout are in prime condition. The English tend anyway to be a little hesitant about using them for the table; that smell of thyme about a fresh-caught grayling that allegedly so captivates the French seems not so persuasive over here. However, since it was Spencer's only fish we didn't like to disqualify it from the evening's menu. To our relief we didn't have to.

'We'll take it back for Puffer's cat,' Spencer said.

We wrapped it in newspaper and when we got back to Oxford Spencer stopped outside Puffer's lodgings. There appeared to be no one at home.

'Put it through the letterbox,' Spencer said, 'and we'll get the porter to tell him what we've done.'

I got out with the package and forced it through the letterbox. I didn't say anything to Spencer but I think there was a bit of physical dissemination as the grayling hit the doormat.

We put away the car and stopped at the lodge to ask the porter to warn Puffer about the fish.

'Dr Pollard's away for a month,' the porter informed us.

'Ouch,' Spencer said. 'Where?'

'In Wales, sir. With his sister.'

'What about his cat? And Blackburn Rovers?' Spencer asked.

'He took them with him,' the porter said.

Spencer turned to me. There was a broad smile on his face. 'I sense, Watson, that we have a case of loss of fragrance on our hands. We shall call it the Case of the Ailing Grayling.'

'Unless I am much mistaken, Holmes,' I replied, 'I believe it has already ailed.'

The three of us went for our medicals in different places almost simultaneously. My board examined me without enthusiasm. I had the impression, even before I produced my specialist's report, that I wasn't exactly the secret weapon they had in mind. The verdict was that I should report again in nine months' time. If meanwhile I could get established in a reserved occupation they'd be happy to leave me where I was. It should have been a reprieve; instead, though it was no more than I had suspected, I merely felt left out.

My mother was pleased, my father thought it probably didn't significantly affect the nation's odds long-term. Get America into the war, he said, and you'd hardly notice the difference. I told him petulantly to go steady on the jokes, this was an upsetting time for me. I produced my college freshmen's photograph and pointed out, a little over-dramatically, the faces of three young men already killed. My father said that in his freshmen's photograph he'd have been hard put to point out three young men still alive.

Henry and Lawrence passed without complications, went off to pester the colonels of some reputable regiments to get provisionally accepted for commissions, and were soon successful. I went down to Dorset to stay on Lawrence's father's farm, with the skies full of aeroplanes and the Battle of Britain at its height. Lawrence seemed cheerful enough, but a little subdued. He was off to basic training the following day. His sister Helen, fifteen, smiling and self-possessed, was back from school. I felt completely at ease with all the family, they had that knack of making you like yourself when you were with them.

'What are you going to do?' Lawrence's father asked me.

'I'm not sure,' I replied.

Mrs Wilkes looked up from her newspaper.

'Why don't we ask Cholderton?' she said.

'Why not?' said Mr Wilkes.

I had no idea what they were talking about, but in that brief exchange they dictated the entire pattern of my life.

'Cholderton' turned out to be the headmaster of a neighbouring boys' preparatory school called Combermere. He was kindly, quite vague, and mad on fishing. He would come over occasionally to fish the stretch of the River Axe that ran through the Wilkeses' farm, and Lawrence and his father would occasionally go to Combermere to fish the river there. Mr Wilkes thought Mr Cholderton could be persuaded, especially when he discovered I was also a fly fisherman, to give me a temporary teaching job at the school. They had staff shortages because of the war and a job at Combermere would install me in the reserved occupation that the medical board had intimated they would accept. In the absence of any better suggestion, the Wilkeses' idea seemed worth pursuing.

Lawrence went off to his basic training, Mr Wilkes rang up Mr Cholderton, invited him over to fish and told him there was a young man staying that he'd like him to meet.

Mr Cholderton was charming and, as Mr Wilkes had intimated, extremely keen on fishing. We went down together to the river, which was separated from the house by two large fields. If this was a job interview it was not quite what I had expected. I explained that I had just come down from Oxford, and Mr Wilkes had suggested that there might be a temporary position at Combermere. 'Could well be,' Mr Cholderton replied, in a way that could equally have meant he wasn't sure about the numbers of the existing staff or that he hadn't made up his mind about my suitability as an applicant. Then he asked me about Oxford, not what subjects I had read, or what college I had attended, but where had been the nearest decent place to fish. I told him about the Coln, which seemed to interest him considerably. He made no inquiries about the other aspects of my university career.

By the time he discovered that I too had chosen a size 14 Red Palmer to match the evening's Cinnamon Sedge, I could tell my credentials as a potential schoolmaster were looking rosier by the minute. When I hooked a fish in an awkward place with my first cast, it was the weight of the job that I could imagine on the line.

Mr Cholderton, without actually saying that he was prepared to give me a trial run at his school, began to speak in a way that implied that the matter was settled. He told me the name of the school secretary, who would 'sort things out'. I supposed that could be a reference to salary, accommodation, terms of employment and so on – all the small print factors that Mr Cholderton tended to look at in the round.

With another trout in the bag, I thought I could go for a definite confirmation.

'What would I be teaching?' I asked.

'Oh, this and that,' Mr Cholderton replied.

You couldn't get anything much more concrete than that.

So it was settled. He caught a smallish trout and was boyishly delighted. On the way back to the house he got mixed up in a barbed wire fence. As I carefully disentangled him he asked me, from an almost upside down position, whether I knew about old Canon Greenwell of Durham, the inventor of that most useful fly, the Greenwell's Glory.

'By name, of course,' I said.

'Well, in his extreme old age he used to be wheeled into the River Wear in an invalid chair by his valet. He was covered in American cloth and brown paper and he caught fish.'

The last three words were delivered like an accolade. I held the wire clear and helped him into the field.

'Good for Canon Greenwell,' I said. 'Let's hope that happens to us.'

The Wilkeses were all agog to discover how the interview had gone. There was a lot of signalling from behind Mr Cholderton as he settled down in the drawing-room for a glass of whisky. Helen was almost caught articulating 'How did it go?' and had to thrust a finger in her mouth to pretend she was having trouble with a tooth. Finally, with the suspense unresolved, Mrs Wilkes devised an excuse for getting us both out of the room.

'Did he agree?' she asked.

'Obliquely,' I said. 'It was rather like attending an investiture when they've forgotten the medals.'

'Don't worry,' Mrs Wilkes said in her capable way, 'I'll get him to confirm it in front of us all and then tell the secretary what's agreed. He won't necessarily remember but he certainly won't retract.'

'Over to you,' I said.

Mrs Wilkes was magisterial. 'I hear it's all arranged,' she said to Mr Cholderton. 'That's wonderful.'

Mr Cholderton looked rather hunted and finally said it would be nice to have another fisherman aboard. I deduced from Mrs Wilkes's wink that this was to be interpreted as confirmation of employment in front of witnesses. She then went through the rest of the business with the orderly power of someone beating croquet hoops into a lawn.

As he finally rose to leave, Mr Cholderton said that choosing the right team was the most important thing in the world.

'After fly fishing?' prompted Mr Wilkes.

'After fly fishing,' Mr Cholderton corrected himself.

I saw him to his car. Just as he was about to get in, he looked a little embarrassed and drew me aside.

'Do forgive me,' he said quietly, 'but I don't think I caught your name.'

'My name is Hartley,' I replied. 'J.R. Hartley.'

35

3
The Holiday Let

Lawrence, Henry and I kept in touch throughout the war, we even managed to have the odd day's fishing when Lawrence and Henry could get leave. The foreboding on the Coln turned out a false alarm. Lawrence had the easier postings, Henry saw some stiff fighting up from Anzio, but both came home unscathed, Henry to become a doctor, Lawrence to join his father on the farm.

I took up my appointment at Combermere. Mr Cholderton seemed to have forgotten I was on approval, so I just stayed on, entrusted with the teaching of Latin and history and some filling of the rather more obvious gaps. The wartime staff were a sort of educational Home Guard, although Miss Hentschel, who made a comet-like appearance through our midst, was an exception. She lived locally and bicycled in to teach tennis and art. Her tennis was fine. I played with her once or twice, without winning a point but quick enough to get out of the way. It was her art that was rather overwhelming – very much, as Mr Cholderton observed, School of Serve and Volley. Things got out of control when she decided to paint a huge mural of a Norwegian fjord round the school hall. Combermere was architecturally not an undistinguished house and Mr Cholderton, who was no Philistine, thought that from a decoration standpoint there was much in favour of the status quo. He asked Miss Hentschel to stop. At this she took offence, refused, and continued smacking on the conifers. There was a brief and enjoyable period when a firm of Chard builders and decorators were blowlamping away at Miss Hentschel's creation on one side of the hall as she defiantly continued on the other. With the last wooden chalet implanted in paint that was so thick that you had to walk round it, Miss Hentschel resigned her position at the school in unambiguous language. Then, pausing only to paint something unmentionable on the side of Mr Cholderton's car, she bicycled into the sunset. We never saw her again.

I wondered sometimes how the school achieved such respectable results. Perhaps it was in part because Mr Cholderton in his eccentric way commanded loyalty. With the administrative assistance of the school secretary, the veteran Miss Brewer, he kept things going happily enough until his nephew returned from the war to take over the headmastership.

I soon realised that our common interest in fishing put me in a favoured position with Mr Cholderton. Our discussions about fly patterns and hook sizes must have infuriated the sycophantic Mr Congleton, whose attempts to curry favour were embarrassingly transparent and consistently ineffective. The fact, too, that I was the one who helped the headmaster teach fly fishing to some of the older boys made me his natural lieutenant, because there was nothing in the school curriculum that Mr Cholderton considered more important. I remember once, just after the end of the mayfly season, he burst into my classroom with a dish containing a two pound trout. The boys all stood up and remained standing while he was in the room. 'Little Marryat,' he said, 'size 14.' There was spontaneous clapping. He looked at me with a fellow enthusiast's smile and I began clapping too. He

37

backed away with his fish like some operatic virtuoso taking applause for his performance.

It was a luxury to have the Axe flowing through the grounds. We had about seven hundred yards in all and I got to know every inch, from both banks. It is the only West Country stream to rise in chalk, on the downs above Beaminster, and is for that reason markedly more fertile than other rivers in the south west. Our stretch was gentle, generally quite deep and slow-moving, bounded in places by reed beds and tall grasses. We fished from the bank rather than by wading, and the handsome surrounding parkland made it an idyllic setting.

The school buildings had started life as a medium-sized early Georgian manor, built in Portland stone with an East India Company fortune by a family called Ledingham. It sat prosperously in its landscaped park, declaring something that the family did very little to sustain; indeed they apparently did not much else than look out of the handsomely proportioned windows until funds ran low at the end of the Victorian era. The daughter of the house, an only child, then married a resourceful parson, the Revd Augustus Cholderton (my head-master's father), whose family had come good selling patented trouser presses to the Army. The Revd Augustus made extensive but architecturally not very harmonious additions to the back of the house and declared himself open for business as Combermere Preparatory School for Boys; and the school soon built up a reputation for sound teaching and a friendly atmosphere, without ever quite hitting the heights.

At the time of my fortuitous involvement there was an additional call on the depleted talents of the staff. Not only were we required to defeat the examiners but Hitler had to be thought of too. We were accordingly allocated various Home Front responsibilities, principally in Civil Defence, which made us feel slightly less useless than most of us undoubtedly were. Air Raid Warden Hartley wasn't the biggest problem to confront the German war machine, but at least I felt I was doing my bit.

I had a tin hat that was on the big side and a gas mask rather more substantial than the civilian issue. My briefing on the protection of the public was substantially self-taught, coming in the main from a series of Wills cigarette cards 'of National Importance', entitled Air Raid Precautions, with a commendatory introduction by the Home Secretary, Samuel Hoare. As a result of this I gave a lecture to the Beaminster Women's Institute on 'Choosing and Equipping Your Refuge Room', though I don't think many of the householders put my recommendations into practice.

We were called in from time to time for Air Raid Precautions drill in Winsham and occasionally for more ambitious training with other units. It was during one of these, on Crewkerne railway station, that my future in Civil Defence was compromised, though Mrs Lester, the delightful school matron, would affirm that my motives – to stop Mr Congleton speaking in an affected and toadying way to the Lord Lieutenant – were not at fault. She and I were at the time operating a two-person stirrup-pump team – myself on pumping, Mrs Lester on nozzle control. For some reason, whether through over-eagerness or lack of dexterity with the equipment, Mrs Lester misdirected the jet and instead of humiliating Mr Congleton in mid-conversation she blasted the Lord Lieutenant's sealyham off the platform. The Lord Lieutenant, abetted by Mr Congleton, got into a dreadful huff and said he would intervene personally with our Area Commander; with the result that Mrs Lester was thereafter allowed to read nothing more warlike than Cash's name tapes, and my services were only deployed in the immediate defence of Combermere.

As it happened, this was an unusually difficult assignment. We were trained to pick out the merest pinprick of light that was violating the blackout regulations and to shout in an assertive manner 'Put that light out.' My dilemma was that in patrolling Combermere I was confronted with not a pinprick but a sea of light flooding out from the headmaster's private quarters. I had to balance the national interest with my own, but coming to the conclusion that the school was not a strategic focal point for either side, I thought it would be insensitive, particularly during the period when I believed myself to be on approval, to put my training into practice.

Matters came to a head one night in the summer term. The sirens had sounded and Mr Congleton and I had helped to escort the boys down from their dormitories to the air raid shelter, which would have been less of an organisational feat had the headmaster not cordoned half of it off for the cultivation of mushrooms. Then I left Mr Congleton to pass round the emergency pillows, which were not much more than sandbags in white covers, put on my tin hat and went outside. The usual blaze of light was issuing forth from the headmaster's uncurtained windows, while high above the school there was the distinctive engine sound of large numbers of German aeroplanes. Half the Luftwaffe seemed to be rendezvousing for a bombing run, probably on poor old Bristol, and the friendly marker, known to the German High Command if not to my superiors in Winsham, was evidently Combermere. My reason told me that in these circumstances Combermere itself was the last place the Germans were likely to attack, but it seemed extremely shabby to be helping them on their way to other targets. I decided I must take action.

I went across to the headmaster's wing and, standing in a flower bed, called up to the first floor window.

'Er, Headmaster.'

There was no reply. I tried again, just a fraction louder. Still no reply.

I rummaged about in the flower bed and found a pebble. Then I threw it up so that it plonked gently against the pane.

Nothing happened immediately and I was just considering

an even more drastic approach when the window was thrown up and two rounds from a shotgun were loosed off not all that far above my head. I spreadeagled myself against the wall and there I remained until a Scottish voice asked through the darkness, 'Who's doing the shooting?'

It was Miss Craigie, the Combermere cook-housekeeper, sturdy, personable and on the road to thirty-five. There was always a little innuendo about her in the Common Room and she was referred to among the masters as 'The Holiday Let'. I asked Mr Congleton about this and he explained, with a rather ungentlemanly smile, 'Get her on holiday and she'll let you.'

I couldn't believe that Mr Congleton, of all people, could be speaking from personal experience. I hadn't much self-assurance myself with the opposite sex but it didn't occur to me that Mr Congleton would be in demand even for spares. The sheer bad taste of his disclosure inclined me to Miss Craigie's corner. This, in retrospect, may have been a mistake. Miss Craigie took a red-blooded interest in sexual statistics and two considerations had come to her attention: first that the male staff at Combermere weren't exactly a crack division and secondly that I was thirty years younger than all of them. It put me in a vulnerable position.

'It's the headmaster,' I called out, 'loosing off at Jerry.'

'Is that you, Mr Hartley?' she said, peering over the flower bed at my outline against the wall.

'Yes,' I replied. 'Hello there, Miss Craigie.'

She stood looking at me thoughtfully, indifferent to the sound of the German aeroplanes.

'I hear you're very fond of fishing,' she said after a while.

'Yes,' I said, 'I like fishing.'

'That'll be fly fishing, will it?' she asked.

'Yes,' I said.

'Will you take me sometime?' she asked. 'I'd love to see how it's done.'

'Of course,' I said.

'My passion's Highland dancing,' she went on.

'Really?' I said. 'I've always admired people who are good at Highland dancing. I'm hopeless myself.'

'Right,' she said, 'that's settled then. You take me fishing and I'll take you Highland dancing.'

The full enormity of this proposition was not lost upon me, even at that early stage and with several squadrons of enemy bombers circling overhead. I guessed that Miss Craigie's recreational intentions were likely to be high profile. The tin hat might come in useful after all.

The president of the Winsham and Chard Highland Dancing Society was Major Macdonald-Macdonald, who had two of almost everything needed for the pursuit except that he was missing an arm, which he was proud to have lost in the service of his country. His wife compensated in part for this by having one and a half times normal-sized feet, so that their joint inventory wasn't all that glaringly deficient; and if enthusiasm came in on the credit side they were actually in front. Even the music, on a piano accordion, was provided by the major's valet-chauffeur, Corporal McVitie, who had fought a short way behind his employer for much of the 1914-18 war – until, that is, the major lost his arm – and had followed him afterwards into civilian life. Apart from the coterie of genuine expatriates enlisted by the Macdonald-Macdonalds, the Society enjoyed surprising popularity among the ageing Southerners, who regarded the dancing as a form of social PT rather than any rapprochement with the Old Enemy.

Quite soon after our encounter under the headmaster's window, Miss Craigie sought me out with a printed fixture list of the Society's forthcoming evenings. She said she'd been in touch with the major and reported that she had a new recruit and the major couldn't have been more pleased. This didn't, I have to admit, encapsulate my own sentiments but I simply didn't have the fire power to deflect Miss Craigie now. So the following Friday evening we headed into Winsham on my motor cycle to trip the light fantastic.

Miss Craigie was on the pillion, crammed into a green satin outfit with a tartan sash, and gripping my waist so tightly that by the time I taxied the bicycle into a wall of sandbags by the back entrance of the Godfrey Garstang Hall, I must have looked like an egg-timer.

I was embarrassed by my appearance. I had asked Miss Craigie for advice on what to wear, and she had advised 'something tidy'. Even guidelines as loosely framed as that represented a challenge to my wardrobe, but I finally called up my evening trousers, a rather small frilly shirt which had for some reason remained in my possession after a play we performed at Arborleigh based on *The Three Musketeers*, a blue cummerbund, and my evening shoes. To make matters worse, in trying to slow down the bicycle before we ran into the sandbags, I caught my right shoe on a metal tongue sticking up from the ground and knocked off the heel. I suppose in other circumstances I could have risked a partially flat-footed performance, but a hasty examination of the shoe suggested that if there were reels on the bill that involved a leap or an eventually down-thrusting cavort I should almost certainly become nailed to the floor.

'Don't worry,' Miss Craigie said after I'd helped her up from the surface of the car park and dusted down the satin outfit with my sleeve, 'the major'll have shoes.'

I didn't quite know what to make of this. Had we been talking gloves, I could see that the major might be carrying over-stocks, but there seemed no good reason why he should wish to part with one of his shoes.

Miss Craigie took me by the arm and wrenched me into the hall. Major Macdonald-Macdonald came up to greet me with old-world courtesy and Miss Craigie explained my problem.

'Myrna,' the major called out, 'have we a spare shoe?'

At this a hefty rubicund woman detached herself from a

kilted group of Society members and introduced herself as Myrna Macdonald-Macdonald. I glanced down at her shoes. They were huge, with buckles on them like roof racks. For a moment I thought she was preparing to detach one, but luckily she presumed that I was after a gent's fitting, and the other expatriate lairds were quizzed in turn about the availability of spare size 9s. They proved to be foolish virgins to a man and I was finally offered a soldierly styling belonging to Corporal McVitie, which had toecaps so astoundingly well-polished that the warden in me wondered if they might be of navigational assistance to German aircraft. I said I couldn't possibly deprive him of one of his shoes. He was crucial to the success of the evening, he couldn't make music standing there like a stork. Not a bit of it, the corporal assured me, it was the very least he could do.

I don't wish to put too rosy a complexion on the evening but I could best describe it as unreservedly terrible. Because I had only a very hazy notion of what I was supposed to be doing, and because I erred on the side of over-commitment, out of consideration for Miss Craigie's bona fides with the Macdonald-Macdonalds, each new dance extended the limits of my humiliation. My worst moment, however, was not entirely my fault. Reels can involve a high content of centrifugal force, not always compensated for by the suction factor of Miss Craigie's presence in the party. It was just my luck, when I'd worked up maximum velocity, to come up against the missing handrail, as it were, of Major Macdonald-Macdonald's unfilled sleeve, with the result that I flew like a cover drive into a bank of hydrangeas that shielded the entrance to the ladies' powder room. The music faltered, there were cries of 'Stretcher party' and Mrs Macdonald-Macdonald and Miss Craigie came hustling across to revive me and assist me back into play. I took up position again, dangled my leg like an injured horse while Corporal McVitie sounded the introductory chord, and then we were whooping and whirling as if there were no tomorrow – which I now began to think an increasingly strong possibility.

Afterwards we had soft drinks and sandwiches and Major Macdonald-Macdonald asked me if I was any relation of the Hartleys of Auchnabannock, or perhaps the Craig-Buchanan-Hartleys of Crossnagarroch. I said not as far as I knew, so he filled me in with a catalogue of anecdotes about various members of those families in case some latent memory might be jogged about my kinship. I felt I was disappointing him when I had to shake my head and admit that no, it didn't ring a bell.

'Did you enjoy yourself?' Miss Craigie called from the pillion as we drove back to Combermere.

'Great fun,' I called back over my shoulder.

I had now to meet my side of the bargain and introduce Miss Craigie to the allure of angling. I sounded out her wishes and she suggested we should go down to the river one lunchtime with a picnic; and afterwards she'd watch me for a bit to see how it was done and then perhaps have 'a wee go' herself. I could hardly take exception to this – indeed it was something of a relief that she hadn't opted to attend the evening rise and expose me to an anxious walk home in the gloaming.

The day was fixed for a Sunday in June when I knew Mr Congleton was on duty and couldn't come spying on us. Not wishing to be seen leaving the school with Miss Craigie, I told her at the last minute that I had to dash into Winsham on my motor cycle. If she could set off with the picnic, I'd join her by the river. I let her see me speed away down the drive and turn out of the gates. Then I stopped in a lay-by for ten minutes before coming back into the grounds.

Miss Craigie had arrived with the picnic. She spread out the rug under a tree and subsided like a languorous puncture on to the ground. As she unpacked the food, which in those days of rationing was a rare spread for two, I noticed uneasily that some exotica from Fortnum and Mason were included in the bill of fare; I hoped that Miss Craigie hadn't on my account made inroads into young Alexander Russell's food parcel which she had taken into safe keeping a day or two before.

'Majestic,' I said as we finished our meal.

'Did you like it?' she asked eagerly.

'Majestic,' I repeated.

I lay back with my head on my arms to endorse the impression of satisfaction. She made a sudden lunge towards me but I instinctively hunched my knees over my body and she went first bounce into the picnic basket.

I got to my feet to discourage a second attempt. 'Time for your fishing lesson,' I said, and began to set up my rod.

She watched me for a while in silence, her head on one side – whether in a consciously wistful pose or because she'd hurt her neck on the picnic basket, I couldn't be sure. Then she asked, 'How big are the fish?'

'Normally about a pound to a pound and a half.'

'That's titchy,' she said.

'It's not enormous,' I conceded, 'but we're not fishing for survival, we're pursuing the angler's art.'

I opened my fly box and went through the patterns for her: Black Gnat, Blue Dun to match the Medium Olive, Little Marryat to match Pale Watery, Red Palmer for the Cinnamon Sedge. I lectured her briefly on Caenis, the 'Angler's Curse', the tiny pale cream up-winged fly which trout love, but which is virtually impossible to represent on a hook.

She looked impressed.

'Did you tie those yourself?' she asked.

'Some of them.'

'Fiddly, aren't they?' she said.

Yes, I said, you had to concentrate.

'Which one are we going to use?'

'I think perhaps a Red Palmer.' I pointed to it. 'It's a traditional Axe fly.'

46

'Who's Red Palmer when he's at home?'

I explained that Red was in this context a shade rather than a Christian name, and that as far as I knew Palmer was a colonel.

'You really know about fishing, don't you?' she said admiringly.

With the rod set up, a conventional split-cane eight-and-a-half-footer, I attached my small Hardy Perfect reel and paid out the silk line, dressing it with grease to make it float. Then I tied on the gut cast, supple from being soaked in my cast wallet. Miss Craigie watched dutifully. Her neck seemed all right again.

'Not very like Highland dancing, is it?' she said.

Comments rose to my lips that would have hurt her feelings. I restrained myself and said with a smile, 'Less music.' Then I told her to stay where she could see what was happening and moved cautiously towards the bank.

Before too long I saw a fish rise towards the far side. He looked really solid. I pointed towards him for Miss Craigie's benefit and raised my finger to my lips. She acknowledged her excitement with a wave of the hand.

I cast, and he rose short to me. I remained kneeling, watching the water intently. Smack – up he came again. I raised my arm to alert Miss Craigie that this was action stations and flicked the Red Palmer in front of his nose. I had him. Though I say it myself, it was a passable demonstration of the dry fly art.

I was fishing with light tackle, and for all Miss Craigie's surprise at the 'titchiness' of the trout, these things are relative. He was evidently an exceptionally good fish, and though my light rod and my three-pound breaking strain cast were quite sufficient for my purpose, they weren't by any means a telegraph pole and a hawser. Besides, with Miss Craigie wearing the L plates behind me I wasn't going to take any chances.

He'd gone quite deep and made for the reeds. Once he

wrapped me round them and I thought I'd lose him, but somehow I got back in contact and eased him clear. Only when I had him almost ready for the net did I look round to court Miss Craigie's approval. As I did so she flew past me like a giant blancmange and crashed unclothed into the river. A descending plume of water soaked my head and shoulders.

The fish quite soon regained the ascendancy as Miss Craigie joined in at its end of the line and began dragging me down the bank. With my rod bent double I implored her to give me some idea of what she thought she was doing. The question seemed only to amuse her.

It was now, just when I had fallen on my side and my line was festooned in huge loops all around me, that the headmaster, rod in hand, came strolling up the bank to join us. He looked at the undignified scene for a while without comment, possibly believing himself the victim of hallucination. Miss Craigie's bosom, bouncing like a cavalry ride past, was competing for his attention, but it was the fisherman in him that finally prevailed.

'Big Craigie?' he asked. 'Size 42?'

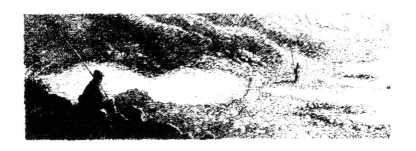

4
Putting in the Boot

Line up all the parents during my time at Combermere and your first choice had to be Mr Ellingham. Admittedly most of them made your selection fairly easy, but Mr Ellingham, without being at all flamboyant, simply looked a success. The headmaster thought he'd bought himself at Harrods. If you had to put your finger on it, Mr Ellingham had finish.

He also had money. He it was who produced a cheque for the entire cost of the new swimming pool before the appeal had even got off the ground; and still waters, as the bursar would keep reminding us with that irritating smirk on his face, cost deep. Those of us who looked upon swimming as more of a threat than a recreation would obviously have preferred to see Mr Ellingham's largesse deployed elsewhere; and as young James Ellingham was one of the boys who came fishing with me, I ventured to joke on his report that we were both looking forward to stocking the new pool with rainbow trout. The rest of the report, both by myself and my colleagues, suggested there was ground to be made up if James was to do himself justice in the coming year's examinations. The unexpected and, as far as I was concerned, fortunate effect of the document on Mr Ellingham was to prompt him to write me a letter wondering if I would consider accompanying them on a fishing holiday in Scotland, giving James 'a little extra tuition between casts'. The venue would be Inverpolly, a lodge they were taking on the River Polly, between Ullapool and Lochinver on the west coast. The sea trout should still be running, there were a fair number of rather elusive salmon, and he could promise me good company. He apologised that the notice was so short. Yes, I wrote back, I should be absolutely delighted.

It was early August 1950 and the school holidays were still young when I went to join the Ellinghams at Euston Station. We were booked on the night sleeper to Inverness and the arrangement was that we should meet each other at the train. My heart was high, but my luck was low. Mishap was on the platform too.

The names of the passengers were put up in the window of each sleeping car, and you walked down to find your compartment with much the same anxiety as a boy locating his dormitory place at the beginning of term. There it was: Lord Justice Grassington, J. R. Hartley, R. Cartwright ... It couldn't be! No, this would be too much. Rosemary Cartwright, my first romance. She of the freckled face and pert chest, arm in arm with me under the stars after the pony club dance. Had fate thrown us together again for romance on the rails – even romance off the rails? (The answer was no. I met R. Cartwright in the corridor. He was a sixty-five-year-old quantity surveyor.) But just for a moment the violins began to play. Distracted, I tripped over a wicker basket containing a child's rabbit which had been left standing on the edge of the platform. I was carrying my suitcase in one hand and my rod case in the other, and as I fell, I instinctively thrust out my rod arm, only to lance Lord Justice Grassington in the very moment of his ascending the carriage step. The rod case somehow slipped up the back of his jacket, keeling him over on top of me like an enormous toffee apple, with the result that we were both floundering on all fours when the Ellinghams came running up to help.

Had such an ignominious occurrence overtaken a master during termtime, the boys would have found it hilariously funny. As it was, James Ellingham was merely considerably embarrassed. He saw it, I suppose, as Combermere exposed to ridicule, and so felt conjoined in my predicament. He looked at his parents in speechless apology. It was the worst aspect of my humiliation. Our relationship was fashioned entirely on Combermere conventions – James would have found it difficult, for instance, not to call me 'sir'. Yet in the circumstances of being more or less hired by his father in the holidays, our positions of seniority were virtually transposed. I needed his loyalty, whether to me or to my identification with the school, much more than my carapace of authority could actually demand.

James helped me to my feet and recaptured the rabbit, returning it to its owner with the assurance that most rabbits had their ears bent in half like that, which in the relief of being reunited with her pet the child seemed happy to accept. Mr Ellingham, with the perfect balance of levity and concern, was successfully placating Lord Justice Grassington, while Mrs Ellingham stood by exuding the balsam of her blonde good looks.

I felt extraordinarily foolish. If this were symptomatic of my fishing dexterity, what would the Ellingham parents be thinking? As we sat at dinner, with the express in full stride, I had a presentiment that a sudden lurch of the dining car would take me by surprise and I would swoosh my entire plate of veal maréchal all over Mrs Ellingham's canary jumper. I therefore abandoned conventional table manners. I hunched my shoulders to cheat the movement of the train and, in my determination to avoid a second fiasco, lowered my face to within a few inches of my plate.

Mr Ellingham must by now have been having serious

misgivings about my inclusion in the party, but he did his best to set me at my ease; and as the threat receded of my deluging Mrs Ellingham with any major percentage of my dinner, I began to recover my confidence. I warmed to these nice people – Mr Ellingham, the socially adroit and polished raconteur, and Mrs Ellingham, always balancing him, quietly assured. I liked the way that now and then she would turn unaffectedly to smile at James; and James would smile diffidently back, with a glance at me to see that I approved these private signals of a happy family life. By the time we swayed off to our respective sleepers and called out our goodnights, I knew that I was going to enjoy myself.

Anticipation is a prime ingredient of the pleasures of fishing. From those first days when I propped my bicycle against the mill race fence and untied my rod case from the crossbar, I have approached the water as if it were some alluring parcel waiting to be unwrapped. As you grow older you contain to some degree the eagerness to get going, you take longer in the preparation, not just because you're conscious of fish lost through casts too quickly tied but because too there is a pleasure merely in extending anticipation. And for me that pleasure was never keener than in the ritual of the Scottish fishing holiday: taking the sleeper north, waking to peer out at that transporting Landseer view and gauge the recent rainfall from the burns that swerved and ducked beside the train; the steward's call with tea and biscuits, 'not far now' to Inverness; then the sigh of stopping, clunk of carriage doors, the clamour of gulls and a vigour in the early morning air.

We were to meet the two married couples in our party in the Station Hotel. Sure enough, when we went into the dining room there were loud cries of greeting from a corner table. I envied them their confidence; in those circumstances I should have signalled and waited to be seen. We joined them and Mr Ellingham effected introductions – Mr and

Mrs Turner (Patrick and Rowena), Mr and Mrs Charlton (Lindsay and Diana). Mrs Turner was thin and rather over-presented, Mrs Charlton provocative and very small. If Mr Ellingham came from Harrods, Mrs Charlton came from Hamleys. All of them, like the Ellinghams, were fortyish.

'This is J. R. Hartley,' said Mr Ellingham.

'Ah,' said Mr Turner, rising to shake my hand, 'Combermere's Mr Fishing.'

I smiled, and then unaccountably allowing my interest in seventeenth-century history to outmanoeuvre my good manners, I drew attention to the coincidence that Turner and Charlton were successive Parliamentary Speakers in the 1670s. I could tell from their faces, particularly the Speakerettes', that they regarded this announcement as a clumsy attempt to show off my knowledge. There was an awkward silence; I felt myself beginning to go red. Mr Ellingham came swiftly to the rescue, and the faltering conversational engines picked up power again.

They chattered on, while I stood there uneasily, trying to look involved but still embarrassed at my opening gaffe. At last Mr Ellingham disengaged us and we crossed the room to settle down to breakfast on our own, with porridge, kippers and whole batteries of toast.

The Turners and the Charltons both had large cars parked on the station forecourt. James and I were to travel with the Turners, Mr and Mrs Ellingham with the Charltons. The hall porter arranged the disposition of our luggage. I could see that he and Mr Ellingham pleased each other, there was a harmony of timing in the way the *pourboire* passed between them.

I was preparing to leave when the Speakerettes announced a change of plan. We were to wait for the shops to open, so that Mr Charlton could buy some shrimp flies, Mr Turner a bottle of vermouth for the evening martinis, Mrs Charlton a bottle of Auld Sporran humbugs for which she'd suddenly remembered a craving, and Mrs Turner three bath plugs, just in case. The Ellinghams claimed to be fully provisioned. It seemed a sensible delay and I accompanied Mr Charlton to the tackle shop and advised him on some extra casts.

We had made our way back to the hotel and I was skimming through the pages of my fishing magazine, when Mrs Turner and Mrs Charlton appeared with about two dozen postcard views of Highland cattle which they settled down noisily to send off to their cronies. Some of the messages were read out and I was sorry to find the standard of their humour disappointing. Nor was I pleased to see, from a sly glance from behind my copy of *The Fishing Gazette*, an invitation to someone in Kensington to 'Spot the schoolmaster'.

With the messages finally completed, there was then a fuss about stamps, resolved by the hall porter, who took over the burdens of despatch. And then we were off. At least not quite, because Mr Turner remembered he had to call the office.

The heavy luggage was in the boot, but James and I had to share the back of the car with what the Turners called the 'odds and ends'. These were more invasive than the term suggests and when Mrs Turner stopped in Beauly and had what appeared to be several hundred yards of tweed loaded on to my lap, my assurance that I was perfectly all right was probably barely audible. I caught sidelong glimpses here and there of open country on the road to Ullapool, but it wasn't the scenic ride for which I'd hoped. Mr Turner meanwhile maintained a breezy patter of observations that could have developed into conversation but for my situation vis-à-vis the tweed supplies. He kept on saying James and I would love this or that, which for some reason I thought increasingly unlikely to be true. And when he told me how much I'd like Legs Maxton, who'd be coming for the second week, I knew he was mistaken. Particularly when Mrs Turner added that Maxton was a scream.

The lodge dominated the Inverpolly glen. From the car

you could see it ahead of you – at least you could if the wherewithal for several hundred pairs of plus fours wasn't immediately in front of your face – for perhaps a couple of miles, crouched white against the hill. The lodge itself was undistinguished, with angular gable windows; nothing at all baronial, more a cross in architectural terms between Council-and-Gretel and Shed. Dry-stone walls marked out an area in front like a settler's compound, tufted with clumps of bracken amid grass cropped short by sheep. Behind the lodge the land rose quite steeply, with deep bracken and under-achieving pine trees, and if you made the climb, the rim of your view turned out to be the top of the cliff and you looked half-left across the sea to the distant outline of the Summer Isles.

Inside, the lodge was an accretion of holiday flotsam, with a staple of more or less serviceable furniture, its upholstery here and there distorted by escaping horsehair. One particular chair in the fishing room had grown so used to exhausted anglers that it had developed a trick, like a parachutist, of buckling and falling sideways just as you sat down. Then the usual bric-a-brac, stags' heads, Edwardian prints of grouse shooting, faded watercolours of lochs, a stuffed weasel, the carpentry end of a swordfish, painted stones, two gigantic vertebrae balanced on top of one another beside the dining-room door, and an assortment of books in the sitting room that could accommodate the most catholic lack of taste.

At one end of the lodge, leading out of the sitting room, was the fishing room – a playroom really, littered with angling paraphernalia. In the corner was a table with a pair of scales: it was part of the Inverpolly ritual to put out your night's catch there and in the morning after breakfast the ladies of the party would file in to exclaim, prodding the stiffened sea trout and lifting them gingerly by the tail. In the centre of the room there was a ping pong table and sometimes Mr Turner and Mr Charlton, accoutred for the river, would pick up bats and play a boisterous rally, guffawing as one or other was beaten by the ball's deflection from an open fly box or a pair of scissors, left on the table top amid the preparations for the day.

At the other end of the lodge there was an annexe, with a flat roof and constructed principally of corrugated iron. This provided three additional bedrooms and was referred to by Mr Ellingham as the 'sleepy lagoon' on account of the accumulation of casual water to be found in the passage when the weather was bad. That wasn't the only occupational hazard. On my second day I came back from the bathroom to find a cow with its head through my bedroom window. It had already eaten one of the curtains and was sizing up the other, but after some puffs in the face from the sitting-room bellows and a verse of 'Blow the Wind Southerly', it reckoned conditions weren't to its liking and backed away.

There were comforts too, and if not quite comforts, sensible acknowledgements of the angler's needs – a good drying room, deep baths of peaty hot water, large thick towels. The London papers appeared a day late, but we kept upsides with world events with the help of both the radio and Mr Turner's morning call from the office, during which we would hear him in the hall saying 'Really?' up to twenty times. Mr Charlton would then be made a party to whatever it was that had so regularly occasioned Mr Turner's surprise. I had the impression, though I am no judge on City matters, that of the two of them Mr Turner had the greater business thrust, accentuated by a tendency on the part of Mr Charlton to get easily outnumbered by martinis.

We were greeted by a smiling housekeeper in a blue overall, who introduced herself, I thought, as Mrs Antler, though when I called her that she laughed and corrected me: her name was Mrs Grantley – with the short Scottish 'a'. She was half of a married couple who had worked for Mr Ellingham's parents and her husband had been killed in the war. She was cheerful and indefatigable, with an aura of unsanctimonious inner goodness that made you think someone had slipped her the secret of the world. She was also a marvellous cook. It amused me to hear her with Mrs Ellingham, because she wore her experience with the family like a row of campaign medals and obviously regarded Mrs Ellingham as something of a recruit. The exhausting fortnight looking after all of us was, I discovered, her annual holiday.

We installed ourselves and unpacked our luggage, then walked down to the river which was in need of rain. Late on that first afternoon James and I went out on the small deep-sided loch no more than half a mile from the lodge. I didn't take a rod, I wanted James to be the fisherman while I set him right and did the rowing. We had also to establish a congenial *modus operandi* for our academic business. The loch, in strong sunlight, made an admirable schoolroom. Latin was one of the principal items on the holiday menu and I devised topical sentences for James to translate, such as 'Surely the schoolmaster has not already lost the oars?' and 'The fish laughs at the boy but does not eat the flies'. James not only sure-footedly negotiated the syntax but upended the meaning by catching two small brownies on a Zulu. He carried them proudly back to Mrs Grantley, who served them up next morning in a suspiciously large fishcake embellished in parsley with the letter 'J'.

I am not a gardener, but I have often felt that it is an occupation that has much in common with teaching. The satisfaction is in seeing your efforts slowly mature; the frustrations are with weed and barren ground. Certainly the Combermere classrooms were rank with juvenile ground elder, though the use of industrial weedkiller or, even better, flamethrowers might not have stood us in good odour with the educational agencies like Gabbitas and Thring. James Ellingham was the sort of boy who made it all worth while –

not overly bright but friendly and inquiring. We had a happy and I think productive fortnight.

James and I were sitting one morning by the sea pool rehearsing the landmarks of the Hundred Years' War and keeping an amused eye on Mrs Charlton's fishing style, which resembled more than anything else the action of a woodpecker, though mercifully trees were the one habitat to which she was not exposed. Conditions were unpromising, the rain that came to our rescue in the second week was still in short supply, the water was low and clear, the wind a breath. There were half a dozen grilse at the tail of the sea pool, which Mrs Charlton was resolutely attacking without any concern for personal concealment, shouting 'Nearly' as she watched her fly pass over them time and time again.

At last she set down her rod, rummaged in her lunch basket and began unwrapping one of Mrs Grantley's venison pasties. She made no attempt to reel in, indeed the rod point was actually submerged, with the line trailing in the water. If you believe in the element of surprise it was a good moment for a grilse to elect to take the fly. It made an impatient sidelong snap, sank broodily down to the very bed of the pool, then, with a powerful shimmy, it was on the move.

So was Mrs Charlton, frantic with excitement. When I could make myself heard above her screams, I counselled 'Keep below your fish', aware as soon as I said it that she would have no practical idea of what I meant. Indeed the principle that rivers flow towards the sea might just at that moment have been too much for her.

I have seen salmon fishing presented – by anglers who presumably wish to appear sporting – as in some way a gladiatorial contest, as if it were a spin of the coin whether the fish lands up on the bank or the angler in the river. In fact the fish has much the poorer of the deal. If it loses the contest, it is effectively dead; if it wins, it is the victory only of avoiding defeat, significant but not gladiatorially satisfying because it inflicts no noticeable inconvenience on the human opponent.

Mrs Charlton's grilse, however, had something to write home about. It had to put up with a shortish spell of energetic discomfort before disengaging itself from the hook, but that was the least it deserved for losing its temper with an obviously suspect concoction that had been noisily coursed past its nose in gin clear water some thirty-five times. On the credit side, as it surged up river it was leaving behind, at varying depths in the sea pool, Mrs Charlton, myself, a rolled gold pencil, a wallet containing a driving licence, a return ticket to London and twenty-four pounds in notes; with still to come a thermos of chilled cucumber soup. That, in salmon circles, qualifies for the Victor Ludorum.

Even though the story is somewhat against me, it would be ungracious to deny the grilse more than these bare statistics of its victory. What happened was as follows. There was at the tail of the sea pool, separating it from the stony beach, a cement wall, rather like a dam, in the centre of which was a gap of approximately two feet to allow access to incoming fish. Though the top of the wall was not all that wide, you did not have to be Blondin to walk along it nor Jesse Owens to negotiate the hiatus. When the alarm sounded during Mrs Charlton's temporary preoccupation with her pasty, I was sitting in the heather on the other side of the pool.

As Mrs Charlton scrabbled for her rod, by now almost totally submerged, she suffered a loss of composure that one must put down to inexperience. Her screams were not a coherent appeal for specialist advice, and though I answered them as such, my succinct replies apparently sounded to her, in the drama of the moment, arcane. Her reaction to 'Keep below your fish' and 'Rod point up' was to run upstream with the rod extended in front of her like a bayonet. The fish then turned and we saw the line arcing back across the sea pool at high speed. At this Mrs Charlton began a return charge, which carried her to the very tail of the pool. With shouts of 'You take it', she leaped on to the wall, along which I was now progressing from the other side, and lurched towards me in the manner of a beaten stag. But our reunion was thwarted by her miscalculation in making no allowance for the gap, and she unhappily pitched sideways into the water at an angle of forty-five degrees.

I was ready for her as she rose like Excalibur a few moments later. Lying on my stomach, with James behind me hanging on to me by the gumboots I had borrowed from the fishing room, I caught hold of Mrs Charlton's wrists with words of reassurance, only to have them die in my throat as my boots, clutched against James's sides, slid off my legs and removed my only guarantee of terra firma. My rolled gold propelling pencil and my wallet, falling from my jacket inside pocket, preceded me into the sea pool and the next thing I knew was the blur of total immersion. At about the same moment the grilse worked its jaws clear of the Mar Lodge, lightly dressed on a number 8 iron, that I had so painstakingly prepared for our lady angler's needs.

By the time we hauled ourselves up to the safety of the rocky edge, the grilse had powered up to the first bend of the river, where it did a single crashing leap, a victory roll as it were, before settling down to rest just off the reeds and to ponder the second puzzle of the day, the verses of 'Stay As Sweet As You Are' that in Mr Turner's impression of Al Bowly were presently keening down from the direction of the Alder Pool.

I could see Mrs Charlton was miffed, from the distance into the sea pool that she kicked the open thermos of chilled cucumber soup. I protested at this, because I didn't want a soup slick to hamper a sighting of my submerged belongings, whereupon she turned on me and addressed me in a way that, though her teeth were chattering too much for me to make out precisely what she said, was certainly opprobrious.

That done, she wrapped the picnic rug round her sopping shoulders and set off for the lodge, the studied purposefulness of her walk diminished by the fact that in the course of her adventures she had lost a shoe.

Loyal James meanwhile had located my possessions. They could be clearly seen on the bottom of the pool in only about four feet of water and with deft manipulation of the landing net we soon had them back on land. Next we recovered Mrs Charlton's rod and disentangled her line. We even found her shoe. The thermos, we decided, must stay where it was.

James reached the lodge some fifty yards ahead of me. It wasn't that I was tired or physically compromised by my foray into the sea pool; I think that the lead in my feet was no more than apprehension about my reception from Mrs Charlton. I might have her shoe, but I reckoned that there my similarity to Prince Charming ran out of steam.

When I came warily out of the fishing room, Mrs Charlton was stretched out on the sitting-room sofa in a dressing gown reading a very old number of the *Illustrated London News*.

'We found your shoe,' I said.

She threw down the magazine and pulled herself off the sofa.

'Oh, J.R.,' she said, 'I'm so sorry.' And she embraced me.

It was chaste, but it was – well, pretty good contact. I hadn't much natural panache in that sort of situation, and besides, there was about six inches clearance between the top of her head and my Adam's apple. I don't know what Alan Ladd would have done in similar circumstances, except that he'd have had the height problem the other way round, but there was nothing in the J. R. Hartley training manual that covered counter-embrace technique with the likes of Mrs Charlton. So I wriggled clear and shook her by the hand.

'No,' I said, 'that's fishing for you.'

Then, on the eighth day, into our idyll came Legs Maxton.

Mr and Mrs Ellingham, James, the Speakerettes and I were sitting outside the lodge having tea. Mr Turner and Mr Charlton had taken a boat out on Loch Sionascaig where they were probably talking about the office. There was a bold afternoon light with perfect visibility; the prospect of Stac Polly rode like Gibraltar in the distance.

'It's Legs,' Mrs Charlton suddenly cried, pointing down the glen.

A car had crossed the little road bridge over the river and swung left up towards us. It was an enormous Rolls-Royce of unimaginable horse power, one of those special models with a great trunk on the back built just before the war to carry you safely into exile.

Oh dear, I thought, this is a scene from Dornford Yates. He would be cross to find someone like me included in it.

The driver had begun sounding the horn, a wonderful Mahleresque note you'd have been glad to have had in your ears as he knocked you down. Either he was deterring the sheep grazing beside the undulating road or he was signifying he had seen us.

I waited with a growing sense of disadvantage. When the car slewed to a standstill on the grass in front of us and Legs Maxton got out, my worst fears were realised. He was fine-looking, fortyish, with strong hair and good hands. He had something more than presence, he was an arsenal of personality. When he began to speak he was assured and witty. His voice was resonant and musical. His clothes were perfect. The man was a nightmare.

He gushed charm over everyone, even over me. I found myself in no time heaving boxes and luggage out of the car – 'Oh, you *are* kind', 'Don't *you* take that', and all the other blandishments that leave a man with strained shoulders and a pain in the side. There were impeccably chosen presents for everyone, except me – not just brute power-spending but thoughtful selections from the best shops, suggesting that he really cared, not about social superiority but about those who helped him exercise it.

Fourth box out was a case of white wine. Since this was obviously for the benefit of the whole household and the shipper's label appealed to me typographically, I made suitable noises of appreciation.

Maxton shrugged. 'Nothing special,' he said easily, 'a case of do or die.'

'The fundamental things apply,' I countered, neatly I thought, picking up the context. He laughed so approvingly that I picked up the box as well.

When we had unloaded everything from the inside of the car, I asked him if there were things in the boot. 'Only European royalty,' he said. 'They can stay where they are.' And so it continued. It was even worse when Mr Turner and Mr Charlton returned from Loch Sionascaig, exploding with bonhomie. Mr Turner had caught two smallish brown trout, Mr Charlton had merely caught the sun.

There were endless confident-classes jokes, and banter, banter, banter. I must have been looking more and more uncomfortable as Maxton held the stage because James suddenly announced that I had translated the main headline in yesterday's *Daily Telegraph* into a Latin hexameter. Even for Maxton this was one coming in under the radar and Mr Ellingham made much of it, not because it particularly impressed him but because, like the considerate host he was, he felt that Maxton was picking up too many of the prizes.

At last I could stand it no longer. I resorted to prayer. 'Dear Father,' I said under my breath, 'you have served up something unworthy in your servant Legs (whatever that may be short for) Maxton. This man won't do, this man is mustard in a perfectly good sandwich, this man is an afternoon spent with the headmaster's mother. Please fashion a trap-door under his feet and remove him from my sight.' Nothing happened. I gloomily concluded that in the avalanche of self-interested requests flowing up to Headquarters at any given moment mine probably wasn't top-of-the-pile material. Maxton swept on through anecdote after successful anecdote, and the Speakerettes, watching him with their faces twitching into giggles, shifted and stirred in their chairs, twirled the gold bangles on their wrists and pushed back the sleeves of their tight-fitting jerseys. Legs Maxton – is there a God in Heaven? – was being a scream.

It continued throughout dinner. When we'd finished, I asked if anyone would be going out fishing. Mr Turner poured himself half a tumbler of cointreau and said he might go and give 'em a bit of Al Bowly up at the Alder Pool. Mr Ellingham was roped in by the ladies to make a four at bridge. Mr Charlton said his face was burning so much that the fish would mistake him for a lighthouse. It was decided on James's behalf that he should go to bed. Maxton declared himself a starter. So the two of us bade Mr Turner tight lines and set out together for the sea pool.

It was a beautiful night, with no more than a quarter-moon – with sea trout a full or almost full moon can destroy your chances of success. There was just a breath of wind to put a slight ripple on the water and keep away the midges, but the sea was calm, wheezing on the stony beach. As we stumped down the rocky track towards the pool there were some encouraging smacks to be heard of finnock on the move. High tide was only an hour ago and it looked as if we had some arrivals newly in from the sea.

There's little to beat sea trout fishing at night if conditions are right. The fish are shy; very often they'll provide ample evidence of their presence but show no interest in your lure. On the Polly we fished with a nine-foot leader with a single dropper, using low-water double hooks, usually about size 10. The patterns that got best results were the old friends – Butcher, Dunkeld, Peter Ross, Zulu, Black Pennell. The sea trout didn't run very large, three or four pounds would be

a very good fish; but even a one and a half pounder fizzing round the sea pool at full throttle was something that stayed in your memory. They had to be eased gingerly down to a manageable netting place and very often we were glad of the double hook. There's a wonderful brilliance about a freshly landed fish, gleaming in the dusk.

Maxton said he'd take the head of the sea pool, if that suited me, and then fish up to the first bend of the river. I hooked a one and a quarter pounder with my second cast, which made a great commotion and probably alarmed the rest. I waited a while for them to settle and then tried again, but to no avail. I repeated the formula several times, and finally packed up around midnight. Maxton seemed to be having his share of difficulties; I heard cries of frustration further up the bank and occasionally I saw a stab of light from his pencil torch as he must have reeled in for repairs. I left him to it. When I got back to the lodge, Mr Turner was in from the Alder Pool. An empty cointreau bottle was standing on the scales. I turned off the fishing room light and made my way to the sleepy lagoon.

The sound of the wicket gate must have wakened me. Having only one bedroom curtain left, I was able to pull myself up and peer out of the window without getting out of bed. Those who have fished at night in the north of Scotland at that time of the year will know that there is a surprisingly short time of total darkness, and certainly I had no difficulty in making out the figure of Legs Maxton going to the boot of the Rolls-Royce and removing from it three packages. I watched him unwrap them. Each contained a very handsome fish. The European royalty seemed to be raising no objection.

It was not long before I heard Maxton going upstairs to bed. I gave him about twenty minutes, then I got up, eased open my bedroom door and tiptoed to the fishing room. There on the table beside my finnock, waiting for the morning ritual, were Maxton's glistening impostors. The dishonour of the man astounded me. I gathered up the fish, went out to the Rolls-Royce and replaced them in the boot. The house was sleeping. I returned to bed and lay there in a state of exultation. Well, well, well, I thought to myself, good old Headquarters.

Breakfast at Inverpolly Lodge was at nine. Thanks to Mrs Grantley's lavish interpretation of our requirements it was fully and punctually attended. On this particular morning nothing would have made me late. I sat down at the table a few minutes early with a cup of coffee and my book.

Maxton came down last and I waited for him to go over to the serving table. I began by asking Mr Turner whether there'd been any action at the Alder Pool. He gave me a thumbs down sign across the table. I could see Maxton waiting for my question with a practised nonchalance. I asked him how he'd got on.

'Beginner's luck,' he replied. 'I had three rather nice ones.'

'Three?' I enthused. The Speakerettes were all but toppling off their chairs. 'Where did you catch them?'

'One just under the plank bridge, the other two up by the reeds on the far side.'

'Gosh,' I said, 'that's smart casting.'

He returned to the table with his breakfast, rationing his smile.

It was all too much for the Speakerettes. 'Come on everyone,' called out Mrs Turner, 'let's see Legs's fish.'

I let them go ahead of me. When I followed them into the fishing room there was already a great flutter.

'Is there a cat or something?' Maxton was asking.

'Perhaps they weren't quite dead,' Mrs Turner suggested, 'and they started to flip flop back where they came from.'

'It's a strong instinct with fish,' I said, 'but they can't always open the door.'

When I looked at Maxton he seemed a genuinely puzzled man. When, later in the day, I happened to see him walking back from his car, he was like a man to whom light has been revealed when darkness is the kinder option. I think I must have smiled because he looked at me with an expression that passed from realisation into something very close to hatred.

Good old Headquarters.

5
Marriage Lines

I suppose it was written in the stars that I should marry Helen Wilkes. When I first met her she was a teenage schoolgirl; when I proposed to her a dozen or so years later, it wasn't that I'd been struck by a single Cupid's arrow. I had so many amatory darts sticking out of me that I was beginning to look like a toothbrush.

The term after my fishing holiday with the Ellinghams at Inverpolly, Helen started to come in to Combermere part time to teach the youngest boys. It was all quite convenient, since she lived nearby at her parents' farm, and she was noticeably good at the job – bright, patient and affectionate. I had some vicarious kudos from her popularity because I had recommended her and because it was known that I was on close terms with the whole Wilkes family. I think it may have made me feel a little proprietorial towards her. I was emboldened to propose.

We were married at the end of the summer term, and thanks to the kindness of Helen's father we had a cottage to live in on the Wilkeses' land. To show that our marriage was made as much in Hardy's as in Heaven, we decided to have a fishing honeymoon in Skye. As a member of the Wilkes family, Helen had been brought up in an atmosphere of fishing fever and was

69

a very competent performer herself. She inherited from her mother, however, the heresy that not everyone wants to talk about fly fishing twenty-four hours a day. To reinforce this opinion Mrs Wilkes would occasionally get up suddenly and leave the room, to be retrieved by one or other of her menfolk – or their friends – with apologies and false promises of reform. Eventually a close season was introduced, in tandem with the fishing itself, designed to appeal to the sporting instincts of the principal offenders. It was only partially successful.

Helen's father knew Skye well and produced a list of potential benefactors on the island which seemed almost to exceed the total population. He then had a field day giving me directions of what to do and where, until I had to remind him politely that we were only to be there a fortnight and he had already given us full-time occupation for about four months. But his advice was invaluable and his introductions awakened a generosity in our hosts that perhaps said as much about Mr Wilkes as it did about themselves.

We kept our plans a secret from the car and coaxed it in easy stages north. Just before Stirling the accelerator cable stuck and we passed through one village at maximum speed, with Helen on hands and knees pleading with the pedals, while I, with my knees raised above the dashboard, steered for all I was worth. But that was the only mechanical lapse; we didn't even have to contend with the car's reluctance to start which so tormented us during the winter months.

Our first night on Skye we stayed just by Portree and next day went up to the Storr Lochs to fish, brooded over by The Storr to the north and Beinn Chearcaill to the west with a wild bleak beauty that could burst your heart. There are three interlinked lochs, Leathan, Storr and Fada, extending perhaps two and a half miles and about half a mile wide. This is water ideally suited to traditional loch-style boat fishing for trout. The boat is drifted beam-on to the wind, sometimes with a drogue – an underwater braking parachute – deployed over the up-wind gunwale. You make ten- to twelve-yard casts with teams of three flies down wind of the boat, then as the boat bears down on them, you lift your rod, dibbling the bob (top) fly on the surface of the water for as long as possible before re-casting. Trout seem to be attracted by the bob fly in the surface film but often take one of the other flies on the way up to it. We used longish rods (ten to eleven and a half feet), a light floating (at that time greased) line, with a twelve-foot leader of three-pound breaking strain. For choice of flies, the general rule is bright day, bright fly. A good choice would be: point – Black Pennell, Butcher, Peter Ross; dropper – Mallard and Claret, Dunkeld, Teal and Blue; bob – Silver Invicta, Kate MacLaren, Zulu. Of these the bright flies are Dunkeld, Teal and Blue and Kate MacLaren.

We caught quite nice brown trout averaging about a pound. That Helen caught more than I did, I put down to chivalry. But it was the settled peace of the place that mirrored our mood, with sunshine all day over the dark, glittering water, and the unforgettable sight of a bitch otter teaching her two cubs to hunt at the edge of the loch. This was Nature with the benefit of scale, very much her own mistress, benevolent today but menacing when the clouds are down and the subtle, restrained colours of the hills drain into a forbidding grey.

The following day we drove round to the west of the island, a leisurely progress calculated to reward the car for its unprecedented run of good behaviour. We stopped for lunch of delicious fresh-caught lobsters and saw a ship standing offshore out beyond Loch Bracadale, below Macleod's unsexy Maidens and Idrigill Point. We thought it might be a slave ship recruiting for the Winsham and Chard Highland Dancing Society, and it would have been a shrewd location for her captain because a good proportion of the Skye population, born and bred for such pursuits, seemed to be sitting on benches, ripe for capture, gazing out to sea. We could imagine Major Macdonald-Macdonald vetting the intake on the quarterdeck, with the faithful Corporal McVitie on accordion. A few brisk eightsomes under the major's critical eye: those that pass muster, into the hold, those that don't, over the side.

It was in the south of the island, at Loch Coruisk, that we ran into Hamish, perhaps the most lugubrious man the world has ever seen. He was a gillie by profession but I think the local employers passed him round like the odd card out in Old Maid. And rightly so, because compared to Hamish the Slough of Despond would have seemed like a funfair.

Loch Coruisk is set in a deep pocket in the Cuillin Hills, which rear up all around it to a height of 3,000 feet. It is a wonderfully dramatic setting, with a sense of timelessness about it that I have nowhere else experienced so strongly. The loch itself is about a mile and a half long, shallow and sandy at the top end with, at the bottom, a narrow outlet to the sea in Loch Scavaig which can funnel the wind in a most unnerving way for the angler in a boat. There are really good sea trout and the experts will tell you that you should always have a hundred yards of line and backing on your reel. It is best fished with a floating line, working the fly or flies back towards you at varying speeds. Opinions differ as to whether you should fish with more than one fly; most people do, but the locals say, persuasively, that they catch just as many fish with one fly as with two. A wet fly is, in my opinion, better than a dry fly, but again there are two schools of thought.

We were promised a day on Coruisk, with the services of Hamish thrown in to man the boat. This is quite a skilful operation when the loch is calm, because clumsy rowing will put down the fish. The boat has to be both rowed out from the edge then backed down and along in a zigzag. As it happened, a light breeze blew quite evenly on the day we fished the loch, so Hamish's abilities or otherwise were not exposed.

We were to meet at the boat at ten o'clock. We came down from the road by the pony path to Camasunary and it is about two miles further on by sea from there. Hamish was waiting when we arrived and nodded a greeting without actually delving into his vocabulary. He was dressed cautiously for a brightish summer day, with defences of tweed and waterproof that would have been more suitable for an afternoon out with Grace Darling. He worked his lips backwards and forwards over his dentures, pulled on a sou'wester, and gazed round at the weather, which to our untutored eyes looked almost flawless. 'Dour,' he said after a while, 'verra dour.'

This was a big surprise to Helen and myself, but we were practised enough anglers not to undervalue local knowledge.

'Not very promising?' I said chattily.

He thought we'd very likely be wasting our time.

Oh well, we said, we'd be happy enough just being out on the loch on a day like this. And we presented him with a bottle of whisky.

'It'll help keep out the cold,' I thought I joked.

'Aye,' he said, taking me quite literally and with no suggestion of thanks.

He helped us into the boat. Before starting the outboard he slowly unscrewed the top of the whisky bottle and took a swig. His face twitched without conceding any expression. Then he even more slowly replaced the cap and put the bottle into his haversack under the bow canopy.

When we reached Coruisk he settled over the oars with a grim expression of suffering and asked us where we'd like to fish. It was a sizeable expanse of water and I had absolutely no idea which parts of it might be productive. Hamish was for the moment keeping the information to himself. Both shores looked much of a muchness, so to break the deadlock

I pointed to the west shore. 'Let's fish down that side,' I said, 'and see how it goes.'

I watched his face closely for any clues as to his reaction. I might have been speaking to a raised drawbridge.

We had a completely blank morning, with no sign of life at all. We put ashore for lunch. Hamish carefully extracted his small haversack from under the bow canopy of the boat and came and sat with us. Helen and I tried to include him in the conversation, but he contributed nothing. From out of the haversack he pulled the bottle of whisky, permitted himself another generous swig, replaced the bottle, and then rummaged about until he hit upon a minuscule pie wrapped in greaseproof paper. He took a bite out of it, leant back on his elbows and announced that where we'd chosen to fish was always hopeless. We should have been the other side.

We looked at him with incredulity. 'You might have told us,' Helen said.

He looked surprised, gave his mouth a couple of slow circuits round the front dentures, and countered 'Ye didna' ask.'

It was unanswerable. I could see Helen was seething, and I thought diplomacy might be the order of the day before Hamish was treated to some robust assessments. I therefore interposed some weak-kneed general comments which were intended to sound conciliatory. Hamish continued to look ineffably gloomy, peering round at the Cuillins as if to prompt some major natural disaster.

'Well, let's make up for lost time,' Helen said. 'We'll try the other side.' She began to wrap up our things in the picnic rug, making a point of including Hamish's haversack so that he wouldn't have to risk being helpful.

'Could you hold the boat steady, Hamish,' she said, 'and I'll load the things on board.'

As the gillie walked away from us, shaking his head at the inhospitable clemency of the summer afternoon, Helen deftly removed his haversack from the picnic rug and put it behind a

rock. Then she folded up the rug again, clambered aboard and, watched by Hamish, pushed it under the safety of the bow canopy.

I hesitated, then my resolve stiffened and with a smile at Helen I clambered aboard after her.

The rest of the day's endeavours were quite a different story, four fine sea trout between us, each one like a blow in the solar plexus for Hamish. Three of them we had in the shallows halfway up the loch, and Helen was broken by another fish, which leapt on being hooked – as sea trout will – and caught her unawares. This at least was cheerful news for Hamish, who must have felt by then that our success was becoming unbearable.

At the end of the day he started up the outboard and we chugged out through the gap of the loch, out of the clutch of the Cuillins and into the sea. Soay, Rhum and Canna lazed in the evening light ahead of us. The wind had dropped, all Hamish's dire predictions were confounded. And he had worse to come. Helen and I, together in the bow, sat huddled in the warmth of our little conspiracy, watching the blue peaks receding behind us and the turning tide clawing at the shore. Then, with the boat's white wake tracking round in a widening arc over the swell, we came into view of the lodge at Camasunary, held in the flat palm of the hinterland between the hills. And we laughed at Hamish's disapproving figure hunched over the tiller at the other end of the boat, and at our pleasure in each other, the time ahead of us, and the spell of the sea and the sky.

The engine died away and we felt the scrunch of the boat grounding, freed for a moment as Hamish climbed out into the water to draw us in. Helen pulled out the bundled picnic rug and stood there with it in her arms waiting to get out. Then, with Hamish standing malignantly by the boat's mooring post, we prepared to make our farewells.

'Where's ma sack?' he asked eventually.

Helen affected dismay. 'It's by a rock at our picnic place,' she said. 'Oh, don't say you want it.'

The gloom in Hamish's voice had a musical quality. He forced out the words. Of course he wanted it.

'You should have said,' Helen told him.

We set off along the steep pony path, five hundred feet up and then on to where we'd left the car. We turned at the top to look back at that stunning view over Camasunary to the Cuillins. Just emerging from Loch Coruisk we saw Hamish in the cockle of discontent, the haversack presumably retrieved.

We watched together for a while with vindictive satisfaction. Then we walked on to the car, in the earnest hope it wouldn't let us down. It started first time and we bumped away round the top of Loch Slapin to Broadford and our friends.

6

Test Guest

As I came into the Common Room the bursar was holding an envelope up to the electric light.

'It's for you,' he said, 'London E.C.3 postmark. One of your City friends?'

'I didn't know I had any,' I replied, wresting the letter out of his hand. 'Who on earth can it be?'

Had I arrived a few moments later no doubt the bursar would have been able to answer that question. As it was, he waited expectantly while I opened the envelope.

'Good heavens,' I said, 'it's from Sir Chips Browning. He wants me to come fishing on the Test.'

The bursar looked impressed. Invitations to fishing headquarters from fast food moguls didn't hit the Combermere doormat every day. Sir Chips had a boy at the school whom I had taught to cast, but I could hardly believe something like that put me within sniffing distance of the Browning Industries' entertaining budget. People like Sir Chips went fishing expensively with Japanese businessmen who wanted to open up the carpburger market. There was no place in that bowl for the likes of me. No, this must be a personal gesture. If so, it was extraordinarily civil.

'Are you making a career in sausage rolls?' the bursar asked.

'No, I expect he wants to follow up my bursar paté idea,' I said as flatteningly as I could, which when dealing with someone as buoyant as the bursar was hardly flattening at all. With that, I turned on my heel as they say, and went off to upset my class about the execution of Charles I.

Sir Chips had asked me to telephone him, which I did. I was a little taken aback by what he had to say. He'd had an invitation for a day's fishing near Wherwell on the upper Test, from an American who was hoping to do business with him. He'd been asked to invite two other keen fishermen. Apart from his colleague Lord Mulchett, there was no one in the higher echelons of Browning Industries who could tell the difference between a Lunn's Particular and a bottle of tomato ketchup, or indeed much wanted to. As I'd been so helpful over teaching his son to cast, he thought I might like a day on the Test in the role of supporting actor.

'But surely he'll rumble us?' I said.

'No, no, no. Just be non-committal and leave it to me. It'll be good fishing and we might get a laugh out of it.'

'But what if he asks me about City things? Talking to me about business is rather like talking to Mowgli about the Seven Years War.'

'Well, would you rather I asked Mowgli?'

'No,' I said quickly, 'it's kind of you even to think of me.'

The performance was scheduled for a date in mid-May, some three weeks ahead. I began to have serious misgivings. Helen, who seemed to be untouched by considerations of business morality, told me not to be feeble. Lawrence, my brother-in-law, thought the whole thing would be 'a hoot'. So, perhaps rashly, I asked the headmaster whether I could have the day off, explaining that it was an invitation from an important parent and the bursar would fill in by taking my class to Corfe Castle and upsetting them a bit more about the Civil War.

'He's going to borrow a Charles I costume from the Crewkerne amateur dramatic group,' I said.

The headmaster looked deeply uncertain. 'I see. Suppose he runs into a Roundhead patrol?'

'I'm afraid we can't count on it,' I said.

The subject of my Test adventure came up regularly, but not normally involving my daughter Barbara. We were all having lunch by the Axe one Sunday morning at the beginning of May when she wondered why, if God loved everybody equally, Uncle Lawrence had caught four trout and I had caught none. It fell to me to put the theological position.

'Because God knows that Uncle Lawrence hasn't been invited to fish on the Test by one of the country's leading industrialists.'

Barbara considered this explanation for a while before raising the canard that if the leading industrialist had known that Uncle Lawrence had caught four fish and I'd caught none, the leading industrialist might have been better advised to invite Uncle Lawrence instead of me. This sounded uncomfortably like both logic and insubordination, so I was glad to see Helen begin to pull her weight and, to take the sting out of the debate, accept a challenge from Barbara to sit for five minutes with a melon balanced on her head. Timed by Lawrence, she won, to warm applause; and as she laughed and raised her hand to take the child's, you couldn't but be sunned by the affection in her face.

There was another aspect of the Test that was causing me concern. The American was going to be exceedingly surprised in the difference in commercial calibre between Sir Chips's two guests. Compared to Lord Mulchett, I wasn't even going to look like the twelfth man. I wasn't even going to look like the scorer. Lord Mulchett's business record was a byword for entrepreneurial acumen. He was the genius behind Snifco, the conglomerate that had grown out of the Stoke Newington Industrial Fertiliser Company. He had been ennobled by the Labour government as a potentially useful spokesman in the Lords, but caused an upset by stating publicly that he assumed he'd been drawn into the political scene simply because he was unlikely to mind the smell. He then went on to fluster the College of Heralds by choosing the title Mulchett of Stoke Newington, with a splendidly heavy-handed choice of motto – 'Thereby hangs a tail'. The public, embracing the music hall bad taste of it all, took him to their hearts.

The bursar meanwhile was maintaining an uncharacteristic reticence about the whole affair. I think he felt I was encroaching on his preserve by rubbing shoulders with the sort of people who fill the accountants' hall of fame. This must have seemed rather a betrayal; and considering that the threat came from me, a betrayal of rather a comic kind.

Not that he was exactly big business himself. He had been a partner in a London firm of chartered accountants before pulling out in his late thirties when his mother left him a lot of money. He talked of leaving the 'rat race' – which is generally a complaint that the rats are picking up most of the medals – and as his firm advised the Cholderton family he somehow persuaded the headmaster, Henry Cholderton (the nephew of my original employer), that he might give Combermere the benefit of his financial expertise. He was installed in a bachelor flat in the old stable block adjoining the school, and took root as busybody-in-waiting. You couldn't actually dislike him, but he was regarded rather like a dart board – full of figures and ideal for sticking things into. Which is why, the evening before my day on the Test, I put my head round the door and asked if there were any up-to-the-minute commercial talking points I should have at the ready. Not that I wanted to know; I just wanted to remind him that I was Sir Chips's man. He put on a vinegary face and said he was rather tied up for the moment.

Apart from its associations for the fly fisherman, there's

something about the Test, through much of its luxuriant course, that makes you stand and look at it. I stopped the car on the bridge in Stockbridge to study the river in its more sedate mood before some soulless hooting from behind had me moving up the broad main street with an apologetic wave into the driving mirror. As I passed the Grosvenor Hotel, I gave the obligatory eyes left to the first floor club room of the Houghton Club, *crème de la crème*, jutting out from the hotel like a coastguard station that has mislaid the sea. At the end of the town I turned left and headed on up the valley to Wherwell. At the river level, poplars, hawthorns and alders were in full leaf now; marsh marigolds flecked the meadows rich yellow. In the villages some of the whitewashed cottages, their Elizabethan oaken frames stained black by later generations, have wonderfully crafted thatch; and now these villages pay the penalty for their picturesque desirability by ceding more and more footholds to the new, substituting for the old country feel a more affluent and received rurality.

I was to meet my business colleagues beyond the bridge over the river at the junction of the road to Chilbolton. Sir Chips and Lord Mulchett were standing talking beside a chauffeur-driven car. I parked alongside and got out to present myself.

They were geniality itself.

'No sign yet of our host,' Sir Chips said. He looked at his watch. 'Any minute now, I should think.'

I felt a bout of panic.

'I'm sure this is going to be a disaster,' I said.

Sir Chips laughed.

'Just keep your head down and don't worry.'

'Do we know what sort of person he is?' I asked.

'He's quite a good businessman,' Lord Mulchett said. 'That doesn't necessarily mean he's much of a tender plant. I think we could be in for the braces and bread brigade.'

The truth was very different. A car pulled up and a man

got out who knew what he was doing. He must have been in his late fifties, good-looking in a patrician sort of way, with well-worn fishing clothes that were evidently pedigree. Mine, by contrast, were well-worn and evidently not. Sir Chips and Lord Mulchett looked as if they'd been dressed up to appear in a mail order catalogue and had to be back in the show room window by five o'clock.

He introduced himself. 'Chester Ellison.' His accent was Boston or thereabouts.

Going down to the river, I knew I was with a fisherman. The others were businessmen out fishing. Mr Ellison talked in language I could understand. There was absolutely no threatening stuff about futures, margins, or home to export ratio; just Kite's Imperial, Houghton Ruby, and the weather. You weren't going to see this one setting up the camp stool and throwing in the bread.

This of course is fisherman's water, the classic chalk stream. At Wherwell the Test has not yet reached the opulent hauls of the Houghton Club water; the fish here average perhaps a pound and a half but run up to three or four pounds. The main river is twenty yards or more wide and relatively shallow, eighteen inches to four feet deep, with a few deeper pools. As in the Itchen and the Kennet valleys, the Test has numerous man-made side-streams, 'carriers' as they are called, with their levels controlled by manipulation of the hatches. They were originally created to increase the productivity of the surrounding water meadows by flooding them in winter; in places the water meadow system was used for the production of reeds for thatching. The 'drowners' who operated the systems were great countrymen and naturalists, but they have long since gone and only the essential hatches are in use now, maintaining a balance in the levels of the water.

The bankside vegetation was still fairly restrained and the riverside paths were neatly mown. It had been rather a late spring and there were still Olives about on the water, which are matched in the artificial versions by Kite's Imperial for the Large Dark Olive and Blue Upright for the Medium. Otherwise I had Black Gnat in reserve and a size 16 Houghton Ruby for the Little Claret Spinner. You get the Iron Blue Dun on this water around the middle of May, but particularly on cold blustery days. I didn't see any about today, which was intermittently sunny with only the gentlest breeze.

'Do you know the Test?' Mr Ellison asked me.

I said that I was mostly brought up in Hampshire, and thanks to two of my father's patients I had done some fishing in a couple of places. I hoped he'd lay off my life history before we got into trouble. To my relief he kept to fishing technicalities, asking my advice on this and that, examining the contents of my fly box.

Everything went well until lunchtime. We were suitably spread out, I had two nice fish, Mr Ellison one, my business colleagues, fishing the carriers, none. When Mr Ellison suggested that we should go back to the village for lunch in the pub, I called out that I had my sights on a rising fish and I'd follow them. I was anxious to avoid any risky confrontation away from the distractions of the river bank.

I watched them set off in the chauffeur-driven car, then I ate the sandwiches Helen had made me, allowed a safety interval, and followed. At least I was able to claim, to excuse the delay, that I'd caught the fish.

The three of them were sitting at a table in the corner of the bar, deep in conversation. I approached with trepidation. Sir Chips stage-managed the encounter very neatly, giving me a quick résumé of their discussion which would seem convincing to Mr Ellison without opening the door for him to address any questions to me. I could hardly believe my good fortune when Mr Ellison expressed his keenness to get back to the river and proposed our respective beats for the afternoon. As we all rose to leave, Sir Chips gave me a con-spiratorial smile.

I let them leave the car park ahead of me, delayed a little, and then drove back the few hundred yards out of the village. As I reached the bridge, they came walking round the corner towards me; and I maintained this interval, which repre-sented safety, as I followed them back across the bridge and into the field which lay between the main river and one of the carriers. It was a triumph of defensive manoeuvring. They were now in the middle of the field, almost a hundred yards away from me, preparing to go their separate ways. Mr Ellison turned to see that I was all right, waved, and then began to walk off towards the corner of the field and the river well above me. I saw him reach the bank and stop to attend to his tackle, probably to attach my recommendation of a size 16 Blue Upright to his leader. It was a gratifying vignette.

I should have enjoyed it while I could. I suppose that if I'd been invited to close my eyes and think of the most unwel-come sight that could possibly confront me when I reopened them, the truth would have eluded my imagination. I should have settled for something by comparison tame, like the sky full of Russian paratroopers or a ninety-foot tidal wave roll-ing up the road from Wherwell or the headmaster's mother approaching with one of her watercolours. But this was in a different division. A charabanc had lurched to a standstill in the field behind me and from it, as from a Trojan Horse, my Combermere class were noisily dismounting, followed by the bursar dressed as Charles I.

It was as if I'd been sandbagged. I sank to the ground and my head wobbled from side to side through some strange immobilisation of the muscles in my neck. The bursar's reprisal had scored a direct hit. Had I been full of steam I think I should have hissed away to nothing.

Some semblance of mental function quite quickly returned to me: not exactly planning but an onrush of instinct such as affects the behaviour of a cornered animal. My one objective was to remain unseen by the boys, because to be discovered by them would be to give the game away to Mr Ellison and to let down Sir Chips and Lord Mulchett – quite apart from conceding defeat to the bursar. I remained full length on the ground under the lea of the bank and considered the geography.

The field was more or less flat, with rough grass and big clumps of nettles, though Regimental Sergeant-Major Harmsworth would have claimed there were areas of dead ground if you happened to be a well-ironed snake. The boys were less than a hundred yards away and were already starting to orbit outwards from the vicinity of the charabanc; if they approached much nearer they must see me. Then, happily, I heard the bursar's petulant voice recalling a group who were getting dangerously close. They were needed as regicides for his Charles I drama.

The only place of permanent concealment that I could hope to reach in time was a very thick tree about sixty yards down the bank. Beyond that there was nothing until the line of trees that bounded the field a further hundred yards ahead. It was the very thick tree or nothing. I concealed my rod and fishing bag in a patch of vegetation and then I went for it, scuttling along under the protection of the bank.

I got to the tree unseen and shot up it like a koala bear. My heart was thumping so loudly that I feared for a moment that my gasps might disperse my cover and I should find myself hunched conspicuously in the centre of a bald tree. But the leaves held and gradually my powers of appraisal were restored to me. I was able to make an assessment of my situation.

The readings were pretty low. I was stuck up a tree without a rod within a whisker's distance of some of the best dry fly water in the world which I was authorised to fish for that day only. Moreover I looked like having to stay there until the bursar was either warned off the private land, realised it was time to be starting back to Combermere, or – most optimistic of the alternatives – was literally executed in the Charles I drama. There would certainly come a moment when he would try to locate me and discomfort me in front of Mr Ellison, but there at least I thought I had his measure.

With a cautious breast stroke movement I parted the foliage in front of me and opened up a window on the outside world. In the corner of the field the bursar, wearing a black high-crowned hat, was organising his play. The cast of youthful regicides were arranged in two rows for the trial, although discipline seemed lax for such a solemn occasion and the charabanc driver looked out of place. I wondered if the bursar was planning a surprise verdict. Having been subjected to several of his theatrical productions, I thought this not out of the question. Artistic licence was very much part of his portfolio.

After a fairly anarchic ten minutes, I could see that the regicides had landed the odds. The construction of the execution platform was under way. Several collapsible benches were unloaded from the charabanc. Once set up, they were surmounted by various unlikely embellishments, such as the charabanc's spare wheel, which the bursar and Rendlesham-Buller were bowling towards the place of execution. It looked as if the Commonwealth could be coming in with a flourish.

The preparation of the scaffold was soon completed. The regicides, joined by the charabanc driver, clustered round with more pushing and elbowing than was probably allowed for in the script. Rendlesham-Buller, playing chaplain, piped up with a valedictory statement. The bursar removed his high-crowned hat and began to ascend the platform. As he did so, one of the collapsible benches proved to be just that, and the whole construction crumpled, bringing down the spare wheel with a resonant thud on the back of the bursar's head. He lolled sideways, then flopped forwards on his face. The charabanc driver turned him over and knelt down to press an ear to his chest.

I thought I should now have to leave the safety of the branches, but in the very moment of my hesitation I saw the reassuring figure of Sir Chips enter the arena, striding back along the carrier to see what was going on. He stood talking to the charabanc driver in front of the prostrate body. The boys were standing by in anxious groups. Together Sir Chips and the driver dragged the body over to the charabanc and propped it in a sitting position against one of the front mudguards. And after a short while the body stirred and came to life.

At this Sir Chips applied first aid, in spite of some opposition from the charabanc driver who was reluctant to see a strip of material ripped off the tail of his white driving coat and wrapped tightly round the bursar's head. Next, flanked by Sir Chips and the driver, the bursar was steered somehow into the charabanc and laid out across the back seat. The rest of the party boarded sheepishly, the driver put on his cap and started up, and the charabanc drove out of the field and up the road to Wherwell. The Trojan Horse had gone.

Mr Ellison, up the river beyond the line of trees, had seen none of this. I lowered myself down from my hideout and walked back along the bank to where I had hidden my rod and bag. Fishing, I reflected, is full of surprises.

We stood together by the cars. Time to go home.

Mr Ellison shook hands and wished me a safe journey.

'Thank you so much for coming,' he said. 'It's a great luxury to have someone who knows about fishing. I do hope we didn't bore you talking business at lunchtime.'

'Not at all,' I said. Clearly he had no idea that I was even meant to be part of Browning Industries. Our subterfuge had been pointless. I looked at Sir Chips. He blinked.

As I set off on the drive to Dorset, the thought of having wasted such an afternoon's fishing hidden up a tree was almost beyond my capacity to bear. But we are taught to be thankful for small mercies, and if you'd like my idea of quite a decent-sized mercy it was the prospect of informing the bursar that his Trojan Horse had been wheeled into the wrong war.

7
The Man of God

My holiday in County Down with Henry Fisk and Lawrence
Wilkes was a fortuitous experiment. Henry, who was still
unmarried, had been lent a cottage with some fishing and
was anxious for Lawrence and myself to join him. We both
had wives and very young children, so we sat around looking
plaintive until we were told we could go. It was new ground
for all three of us and the novelty took us slightly by surprise.

It was right at the end of July. The cottage looked out
over what the songsters commemorate as the Mountains of
Mourne. There is a local dictum that if you can't see them,
it's raining; if you can, it's about to rain. But since our fishing
hopes depended principally on a spate river, the Shimna, we
weren't going to be disappointed by rain. Nor were we.

On our second day at the cottage Lawrence mentioned to
the keeper of the local general stores, Big Billy McGuirk, that
we were there to fish. At nine thirty the following day the
plumber unexpectedly appeared and began imparting local
knowledge. Halfway through his dissertation the postman
called, although we had no letters, parked his van outside
with the door open and the engine running and stayed to
talk. He was still talking when the plumber suddenly remembered he was due at the schoolmaster's house an hour ago

and left in a rush, taking, as it turned out, the postman's van in preference to the bicycle on which he had arrived. This meant that when the postman decided, in the fullness of time, he should be getting on his way, that particular option was denied him; so he settled down for a further chat until the plumber returned with his van. By now they both felt able to accept our offer of a small dram, and as this was dispensed we were joined by the local man of God, who commented favourably on the fortunate timing of his call and agreed to make up the party. As luck would have it, who should now appear but Big Billy McGuirk with the groceries. He greeted the others most cordially and thought he could just spare a moment to drink our good health. Lawrence, feeling now like the Pied Piper of Hamelin, went outside and looked nervously up and down the road to see if a further posse had got wind of our arrival.

What we all had in common was a passion for fishing and the conversation turned lengthily on aspects of the sport. The conviviality of the occasion crept up on us and we rather lost track of the time. When the postman finally left to complete his round – and he was the first to leave, or at least try to leave – he found that the van had now run out of petrol because the plumber, anxious to maintain the status quo, had left it as he found it – with door open and engine running. This was an administrative reverse which called for discussion, so the postman rejoined us to ask our opinion on whether it was better to throw away the undelivered letters or wait till Big Billy could take the grocery van down to Joe Geraghty's garage to pick up a can of petrol. In a prissy way I told him the latter was the only possible alternative. He cheerfully agreed with this and so did Big Billy, who after an hour or so left for the garage but for some reason, whether forgetfulness or accident we never discovered, failed to return. The plumber then gallantly agreed to bicycle to the garage and fetch the petrol, but though he did reappear after a very long interval it was only with the news that the garage was closed and Joe Geraghty wasn't at home to open it up again. Since the postman was by now completely plastered it didn't much matter anyway. Eventually Lawrence and Henry syphoned some petrol out of our hired car into the postman's tank, then, with the plumber's help, they bundled him into the back of his van and Lawrence, with Henry following behind to bring him back, drove the van down to the village and abandoned it outside the post office. In their absence I was unable to hold the plumber's attention and after a loss of concentration he spent the night face downwards on the lawn, to be aroused the following morning by none other than the postman, who – although we still had no letters – was calling in to say thank you for a very congenial day.

We accumulated a variety of invitations during our day of involuntary entertaining. The man of God seemed to have access to most of the fishing in the province, and I wondered whether the concept of private property conflicted with some wider spiritual view he might hold about ownership. He and the plumber took us all as guests on Loch Island Reavy, the very pretty Belfast Angling Club water to the north of the Castlewellan – Rathfriland road, which skirts along the north side of the Mournes. I say 'guests', but I doubt very much if they were members in the first place. They were completely unembarrassed when I caught them worming. 'Gardener's Fancy,' said the man of God, 'you can't beat it.'

The man of God must have been in his early forties. He was short and stocky, with a brisk walk and an air of detachment. Sanctity was not the first thing that struck you on making his acquaintance, but he busied himself among the community if not always exactly in its service. He was very much part of the local scene.

So was the plumber. Indeed had you dressed both the man of God and the plumber in identical, non-ecclesiastical outfits (which nevertheless allowed for the fact that the plumber was almost a foot taller), nineteen people out of twenty would have supposed that of the two the plumber was the man of God. And if, amazed at the truth, you then drew out your goodnessometer to verify the choice, its readings would have supported the false conclusion reached by the majority.

In return for their invitation to Loch Island Reavy, they and the postman accompanied us, uninvited, on our first outing on the Shimna, where we were authorised to fish through the good offices of Henry's friend who owned the cottage. This was not a success. The postman was very excitable and spent his time trying to foulhook salmon with a murderous triple hook that wouldn't have been out of place in the Chamber of Horrors. The man of God and the plumber, both equipped with stout sea-fishing rods, kept arcing in 'a decent bundle of worms' which hit the water with a resounding splash and did nothing for our chances with the sea trout. We had a hurried council of war and Henry was deputed to explain that our different preferred methods weren't compatible and at the risk of seeming churlish we'd have to insist on trying our luck at different times. This was received understandingly by the plumber and the postman, less graciously by the man of God. However, with a little evasiveness about our plans, we got our own way.

The Shimna is a short river, no more than about ten miles long. It rises on the eastern slopes of the Mourne Mountains, in the shadow of Slieve Donard, and then tumbles down to enter the sea at Newcastle, at the south end of Dundrum Bay. It is very much a spate river, rising and falling sharply in response to rainfall in the Mournes. For the greater part of its length it is a bruising, bustling affair, plunging over waterfalls, sweeping round rugged grey rocks, iridescent pale green in its shallows and cascades, dark but clear in its pools, many of which are protected by the steep-sided ravines, ten to twenty feet deep, in which they lie. It is a narrow river, barely twenty feet wide anywhere, until it slows and steadies a couple of miles from the sea.

Much of its busy descent is through the Tollymore Forest, a deep pine forest which closes darkly down to the water's edge. Though there can be fine runs of salmon, it is virtually impossible to fish the Tollymore Forest water with the fly. Leaving dynamite, poison and sniggling aside, the only way to extract a salmon is with a long rod (twelve to fourteen feet), a fixed-spool reel loaded with twenty-pound breaking strain nylon, and a treble hook. You thread the line through the rod rings and tie on the treble, whch you load with worms. Then you wind the hook right up to the tip ring, lie on a ledge overhanging a pool, push the rod tip down on to the water and rub the worms up and down on a salmon's nose until it gets so angry that it grabs them. Then you hang on as best you can until you or an accomplice are able to gaff or net the fish.

But that is poacher's talk. The old firm of Fisk, Wilkes and Hartley, purists all, were after the sea trout. When there was enough rain to fill the river, which there was when we were there, you could expect excellent runs of sea trout from July onwards. Otherwise the seals in Dundrum Bay gorged themselves on fish waiting to run upstream.

Once we had isolated ourselves from the local enthusiasts, we had some first-class sea trout fishing on the lower reaches and on the estuary itself on a rising tide or at the top of the tide. Night fishing was very much more effective than fishing in daylight. We would make a daytime reconnaissance and then wait until it was completely dark before approaching any of the pools we meant to fish – a full or almost full moon could ruin any chance of success. We used a nine-foot leader with a point fly and a single dropper; the fly patterns were Butcher, Dunkeld, Peter Ross, Teal and Blue and Zulu, all on low-water double hooks, sizes 8 to 12.

The penultimate night of our holiday was the most success-ful. Unhindered by our less orthodox friends, we had twelve sea trout between us and returned to the cottage tired but in good spirits at about half past two.

Soon after half past six I was woken by violent banging on the front door. I had the bedroom at the front of the cottage. I went to the window. Below me I saw the man of God, peer-ing through the letterbox.

'What's the trouble?' I called down.

He shot backwards two or three paces, still in a stooping position, then looked up towards me. In contrast to his ham-mering on the door, from the way he now deliberately kept his voice down he seemed to be anxious to avoid a more general disturbance.

'Could you do us a kindness?' he called up to me. 'There's a drowned fellow fell in the falls.'

Quite apart from the syntax, this sounded very much like an emergency.

'I'm coming down,'I said.

I pulled on my dressing gown and hurried downstairs. As I opened the front door he strode in past me into the sitting room. I followed him in.

'What's happened?' I asked.

His answer was only fractionally amplified from the mes-sage he had called up to my bedroom window.

'There's this drowned fellow fell in the falls.'

'Where?'

'Up Tollymore.'

'Is he dead?'

'Dead as a plank.'

'How did it happen?'

'He fell in the falls.'

'Who is he?'

'He's not from these parts. He's a friend of the plumber's cousin.'

'What can we do for you?'

'Could you and Mr Wilkes come and help us get him out?'

'Of course,' I heard myself say. 'But don't we need Henry Fisk? He's a doctor.'

He made a quick negative movement with his hand.

'No, no,' he said, 'we want to keep it unofficial.'

The situation seemed to be deteriorating by the moment; but I could hardly refuse him.

'Just let me put some clothes on,' I said, 'and wake up Lawrence. I'll be with you in a minute.'

'God bless you,' said the man of God.

Lawrence was startled to be told we were just off to fish a corpse out of the Shimna, but got up in a sort of trance and appeared downstairs in a commendably short time. He exchanged a strained greeting with the man of God.

We went outside where there was a pickup truck parked. In the back were five salmon of about eight pounds each, some fishing gear, a length of rope and a set of number plates.

'I'll lead the way,' said the man of God.

Lawrence and I followed in our car, up into the Mournes, until we came to a lay-by where the man of God's own car was standing. He brought the pickup to a standstill and we parked beside him. Then, taking the rope from the back of the pickup, we walked down through the darkness of the forest and emerged beside the Shimna. Standing by the bank waiting for us were two men. They were both in their thirties, rough-looking, tired and sullen.

It was not difficult to see what had happened. There was an overhanging bank just above the falls; the victim must have lost his balance and been carried down by the force of the river, probably being knocked senseless as he was swept away.

The man of God pointed into the water. We craned cautiously forward. Two or three feet below the surface of the river we could make out the body of a man held by the

force of the current against a rock. The image was distorted by the turbulent water, but we could see his legs were trailing out on one side. His head was bent into his chest and one arm, thrust out the other side, was stirring uselessly against the far side of the rock.

It would be hard to imagine anyone less suited to such a crisis than myself. Lawrence, by contrast, was admirable – strong, decisive and practical. He gave the orders, the rest of us, even the two strangers, silently obeyed. After almost ten minutes, buffeted by the tumbling river and roped for safety to a tree, he managed, at about the twentieth attempt, to get a noose around the dead man's legs and pull it tight. Slowly we hauled at the rope, felt the force of dead weight as the body slipped clear of the rock, and then together we pulled in our gruesome catch and laid it, oozing, on the bank. One of the poachers knelt and turned it over. The face, horribly bruised, lolled suddenly towards me, fixing me with its sightless eyes. It was the stare of troubled death. There was a futility about it that cut me to the heart.

I stood there, ashen. Not for the first time I felt a sense of foreboding.

'Have we something we can carry him down on?' Lawrence asked quietly.

'Leave him with us,' the taller of the two poachers said. It was the first time I had heard him speak.

Lawrence started to protest, but the man cut him short.

'Leave him,' he said.

So we left him and walked back through the forest with the man of God. None of us spoke. There was an oppressive containment about the surrounding pines, deadening our footfall, as if there were some malign force loath to relinquish the secret we carried out to the morning. When we reached the cars, the man of God turned to us, looked rather shifty, and extended his hand.

'A bad business,' he said. 'Thank you both for your help.'

We shook his hand. As he got into his car Lawrence opened the passenger's door and told him we'd call in at the police station and give them a statement. The man of God nodded.

'And,' Lawrence added, pulling out a salmon that was partially concealed under a sack on the car floor, 'I think we'll give this to the cottage hospital.'

8

The Holdenhurst Bombardment Cup

My invitation to fish with General Holdenhurst on the River Wylye was delivered to me at school by a despatch rider. It contained the time, date and place of meeting, endorsed by six-figure map references and topographical notes, arrangements for lunch and tea, and the times at which transport would arrive to collect me from Combermere and would expect to deliver me back. As I stood reading the document on the school steps, the bursar, who took a friendly interest in other people's correspondence, came up to see what I'd got.

'An invitation to fish with General Holdenhurst on the Wylye,' I said. 'I hope the Russians don't make their move when we're down on the bank.'

The bursar pointed cryptically into the sky.

'They'll have read that letter by now. Fine day, you standing out of doors. You'll have your name on the missile list by lunchtime.'

'Ought you to be seen talking to me?' I asked.

'They probably know about me already. I tell everybody their tanks won't start.'

'Won't their tanks start?'

'Not every time. Does your car start every time?'

'My car starts rather rarely. But I hadn't realised the Russians were depending on it for the subjugation of Europe. They certainly haven't told me.'

The bursar shook his head at my muddled grasp of the scenario.

'The tanks' starting performance won't be that much better than your car, and they'll have to stop loads of times before they reach Calais. What happens? The whole place is littered with broken down tanks.'

I liked the idea of all those tank drivers having to thumb through the local equivalent of Yellow Pages for Invasion Start. But wasn't the bursar overlooking something?

'They surely have army mechanics?' I suggested.

'Of course they do,' replied the bursar, 'but they're useless.'

'How do we know they're useless?'

'Because the tanks don't start.'

There was a sweet logic to this. We went indoors and left the Russians to think that one out on their own.

The bursar said he'd watch the papers for reports of troop movements in the East or for sudden activity in the Russian towrope industry. Closer home the only unsettling development was the arrival of a temporary groundsman with a Dorset accent so broad that the bursar said it could only have been learnt in spy school. Significantly, he couldn't start the mowers. He didn't look much more alarming to me than most of the morons already permeating wide areas of British employment, though that didn't necessarily mean he wasn't receiving instructions from Moscow Control – there was no reason why the Russians shouldn't have staffing problems too. Anyway, I thought I could cope with him. He might come lumbering at me with a hammer and sickle, but he certainly wasn't a telescopic sights artist who'd fold me up from a thousand yards. All I had to do was to give him a wide berth.

Meanwhile the bursar occupied himself concocting fantasies about the Russian interest in my outing on the Wylye. I pointed out to him that all I had done was to give General Holdenhurst's godson some innocent instruction in dry fly fishing. Hardly militarily crucial, and if the Russians didn't approve of fishing, the first thing they could do was to stop their trawlers hoovering the ocean until there wasn't enough left in the water to interest a stray cat.

These arguments made no impression on the bursar. He panicked my class one morning by calling out to me, just as I was going into school, 'Keep away from the window. Give him an awkward shot.' The boys didn't like the sound of this at all. They herded down to the far end of the classroom – five of them on the floor – and refused to move until I rather disloyally threw doubts on the bursar's sanity.

The excitements rose and fell, but at the appointed hour on the appointed day the staff car drew up at the school door and a soldier jumped out, a model of manners and deportment, to introduce himself as General Holdenhurst's driver.

I stooped to pick up my rod and fishing bag from the steps.

'Let me take those, sir,' he said, as if I were dreaming of preventing him.

He shoehorned me into the back of the car and slipped into the front with such economy of movement that I wondered if he had been trained to such physical self-possession or whether it was something that came naturally to him and General Holdenhurst had selected him because of it. His neck, exhaustively barbered, thrust up in front of me like a young tree from the khaki confines of his collar. He spoke only in answer to my questions. He drove impeccably. We were due to meet General Holdenhurst on the bridge at Great Wishford at eleven o'clock. At eleven o'clock precisely we were there.

There were several military vehicles parked on either side of the bridge. General Holdenhurst himself, surrounded by a group of acolytes, was leaning against the parapet. Tall, handsome, and with the habit of command, I could see at once he represented a colossal problem to insurgent forces.

As I got out of the car, he came to greet me, hand outstretched.

'Holdenhurst, boss soldier,' he said.

'J. R. Hartley,' I replied, omitting any vocational description.

'You've done wonders for my godson Roderick.'

'I wouldn't say that,' I said, although on reflection I probably would. 'He'll make a good fisherman; he's patient and dextrous.'

'He's a nice boy,' the general said.

'He's a very nice boy,' I agreed with knobs on.

The general gave a that's-settled-then grin to the assembled company and said we should be getting along.

'Where's the johnny with the map?' he asked.

A captain stepped forward and identified himself as Sheldrake's adjutant. I established from the burst of interrogation that followed that Sheldrake was the code name of the gunnery commander and that it was he who had arranged for us to fish on the Wylye. Sheldrake's adjutant had the map reference obtained from his superior and was ordered to lead the way in a jeep. We followed in convoy.

It surprised me as we passed through the village of Great Wishford that we continued under the railway bridge rather than taking the road to the right down the Wylye Valley. We drove almost two miles to a clearing in Grovely Woods and stopped. Sheldrake's adjutant announced we were at the designated map reference. The location was most attractive, but in the absence of any water not easy to fish.

General Holdenhurst wasn't pleased.

'I thought Sheldrake said we were somewhere just above Great Wishford.'

The adjutant looked again at the map and confirmed this was the location he'd been given.

'Get hold of him,' General Holdenhurst said abruptly, 'and ask what the hell's going on.'

The adjutant said that Sheldrake would be up at the ranges. He'd try to get him via headquarters. He went to the jeep and started wireless transmission. Very soon, from the upward gesticulation of his thumb, it was apparent that Sheldrake was in contact. We heard a good deal of 'Wilco', 'Say again, over', and then the adjutant came bounding across to confirm there'd been a mis-transcription and yes, the general was perfectly correct, we were supposed to be just above Great Wishford. The convoy set off down the hill. From the direction of Larkhill we could hear firing on the ranges. One particularly heavy rumble suggested that high explosive to the value of my annual salary had just been despatched towards its target. If Sheldrake's map reading was running true to form, that could mean one less village on the Plain.

The Wylye runs down from Warminster to the Wiltshire Avon along the valley that bears its name, maintaining a surprising independence from two roads and the railway. It isn't even a particular feature of the villages that mark its course – Sutton Veny, Boyton, Stockton, Wylye, the Langfords and Great Wishford – though from the minor road that links the villages you can detect its presence from the alders and white willows on its banks. At the edge of Great Wishford it relinquishes its privacy to run close beside the road, a chalk stream of perhaps a dozen yards across, clear pools between lithe weed; and then, declaring itself more openly, it curves round to the right to Wishford bridge and steers on down to Wilton.

The convoy stopped at the edge of Great Wishford. General Holdenhurst and I crossed the wooden footbridge and walked up along the northern bank, with the driver in attendance carrying our things. There was an impression of military presence all around, discreet but reassuring.

After a short distance the general studied the water and halted.

'Shall I stay down this end, just in case they want to get hold of me in a hurry?' he suggested. Oh my God, he knows something, I thought. 'That's fine by me,' I said in as even a voice as I could manage; and I walked on up the bank.

It wasn't easy. I saw one or two fish rising in midstream which I suspected would be grayling; and so it proved. When a fish took me in a fairly weedy place I thought I should have to resort to sidestrain to keep him clear of trouble, but – as is the way with grayling – he didn't go to weed and I had him out without much difficulty. General Holdenhurst, fishing below me, was not so lucky and lost a brown trout in the weed.

We had been fishing I suppose for an hour when a team of soldiers, under the command of an NCO, ran across the footbridge and into the field behind me carrying a very large square board. They halted, lowered it on to the ground, about turned, and doubled off again. I assumed that this must be a platform on which lunch would be taken. Had I been on my own I should have been quite happy just sitting on the grass; and it set me thinking about the nuances of seniority and what an administrative headache they must sometimes be. Unless General Holdenhurst, I reflected, eats his lunch with me in the open field seated at a table fitted up with silver cutlery and crystal glass, how can you downgrade the lunching facilities of all the ranks junior to General Holdenhurst without getting reduced to a standard that would invite a mutiny? If General Holdenhurst sat down in the field, taking his chance with the red ants and the cow pats like the rest of the civilian population, it would mean that the average private soldier, to maintain the relation between gradation of rank and standards of eating, would have to be picked up by the ankles and dunked into a saucepan of lentils.

My reflections were interrupted by the arrival on the other side of the river of a Saracen armoured troop carrier. I saw

General Holdenhurst stride across the footbridge. The back doors of the vehicle were opened for him by an orderly, and closed again behind him. I hoped this wasn't Red Alert.

I continued casting, reckoning that merely out of good manners General Holdenhurst would have me taken to the safety of a military bunker. But I had to feel uneasy when a helicopter flew in from our left; and uneasier still when it landed on our lunch table. The force of the rotating blades whipped up the surface of the river and threw my tackle into a hopeless tangle. At the same moment General Holdenhurst burst forth from the Saracen in full military gear. He had evidently been using the vehicle as an armour-plated changing room. He came back across the bridge and beckoned me over. I was prepared now for the worst. He said we were going up to the ranges for the final of the Holdenhurst Bombardment Cup. He'd arranged for us to have lunch up there after the presentation. Then the helicopter would bring us back to the river. It seemed that what I had assumed to be the lunch table was no more than a marker after all.

I was helped aboard the helicopter, the pilot revved up and we were snatched into the air. I sat there in huddled terror, careful not to look even towards the window, let alone out of it. General Holdenhurst was entirely relaxed. He turned to smile reassuringly at me from time to time, but with my features clamped into the expectation of imminent impact I was unable to respond.

We landed at the ranges. The general skipped down from the helicopter and I fell after him in front of a fairly substantial crowd. A military band struck up a selection from *Iolanthe*. In front of us stood a table with eight chairs ready for the top command. Behind were two long benches for the next in line and guests. In the centre of the front table stood the Holdenhurst Bombardment Cup.

The first person to catch the general's eye was Sheldrake. I detected tension between the two men; General Holdenhurst had not taken kindly to Sheldrake's blunder and Sheldrake was out to make amends. He hoped our fishing was going well. If anyone appeared asking about tickets, we should mention his name. He warned us that there was occasional checking up on game-fishing licences, but he assumed that these were all in order. At this General Holdenhurst looked a little wary and said, no, now Sheldrake mentioned it, his wasn't, and I remembered guiltily that my own hadn't been renewed. Sheldrake reassured us, but advised us to bear it in mind. Then his wife and Lady Holdenhurst appeared and we all shook hands.

The ladies made an arresting picture. Lady Holdenhurst was superlative, fashioned by craftsmen, built to outperform. Shelduck was the model army wife. She looked good but in no way trouble, with a quiet, attractive way about her and a loyalty to her husband that made you wonder if Sheldrake might not be as lightweight as he appeared. After being endlessly polite to senior officers to heave her husband up the promotional ladder, she was now more often re-dispensing dignified civility to the younger officers whose ascent had only just begun. I sensed a slight wistfulness in her view of Lady Holdenhurst, not from any reservations on a personal level – because Lady Holdenhurst must have seemed to anyone delightful – but because of their respective positions on the board. It seemed to me that they were both very much married to their respective husbands' ranks.

The social interchange completed, the brass buckled down to the business in hand – finding the winner of the Holdenhurst Bombardment Cup. And here friction almost immediately arose betweeen Sheldrake and the general. On the face of it the cup seemed to have been narrowly but fairly won by the unit under Sheldrake's command, in preference to a territorial unit called the East Breconshire Sharpshooters. Perhaps the general wanted to encourage the territorials, or perhaps his decisions were coloured by Sheldrake's miscalculation in landing us in Grovely Woods. At any rate he decided, after hearing the case presented by the Sharpshooters' colonel, that each unit was entitled to a 'warm up' round of firing which shouldn't count towards the final score; and that on this basis the salvo at the start of the morning which had been two and a quarter miles off target could be dismissed as a legitimate 'loosener' from the East Breconshire marksmen. In the light of this ruling, unpopular though it obviously was with Sheldrake, the general was able to call for a shoot off, with rules of what he infelicitously described as 'sudden death' – or first team to lose a round loses. Would they like to spin a coin to see who started? The colonels tossed. The Sharpshooters were to fire first.

'Hoist flags,' General Holdenhurst ordered.

There were two flagpoles adjoining the cup presentation area, on which the flags of the two finalists were now hoisted. The flag of Sheldrake's team was a blue and red affair with an elaborately embroidered cannon with a huge puff of smoke coming out of it, and the legend below 'Steadfast in Bombardment'. The Sharpshooters' flag was dark green with three leeks tied together with a gold bow. Their motto, which particularly caught my attention, was 'Nunc pollicibus venimus demissis'. I turned to the Sharpshooters' adjutant, Captain Williams, and asked him why they'd chosen it.

He looked pleased. 'That's observant of you,' he said. 'There's a story attached to that.'

'Really?' I said.

'Yes,' he went on, 'we advertised for a motto, and a chap from Merthyr Tydfil sent it in. It means "Now we come to the uxorial leeks".'

I considered this for a moment. Then I asked him, 'Which is the word that means "leeks"?'

He made a face. 'Good question. It must be the one beginning with "p". Yes, because "demissis" must be "uxorial", "nunc" is "now" and "venimus" is "we come".'

'No,' I said, 'he was having you on. "Pollicibus" is the ablative of the word for "thumbs".'

'Thumbs?' echoed the adjutant. 'Are you sure it can't sometimes mean "leeks"?'

'Not as far as I know,' I had to tell him. ' "Nunc pollicibus venimus demissis" is the processional chorale from a seventeenth-century Crucifixion mass. It means "Here we come with thumbs descending".'

'Blimey,' said the adjutant. 'The colonel'll have a fit. It's a sort of Desert Island Discs thing, is it?'

We were interrupted by an ear-splitting explosion as the first salvo of the final was loosed off just in front of us. I cowered behind Lady Holdenhurst. It seemed to me extraordinary that the general could consider this a spectator sport. After a short while there was a loud cheer as the observers announced 'Direct hit.' Goodbye Devizes.

Even with my hands over my ears and a crouching position under the table, I felt that I must fall victim to neurasthenia should the shoot off last more than a few rounds. The power of the guns took you by the shoulders and shook you like a rat. After each round I dreaded the cheer and counter-cheer that signified that the contest was still undecided. Finally I heard over the tannoy the blessed announcement 'Miss'. Sheldrake's men had failed to make contact with the distant ruined tank hull that the Sharpshooters' package had made to hop like a frog.

There was pandemonium. The strains of 'Land of My Fathers' spread like a grass fire through the crowd. The band broke into a selection from *Iolanthe*. I emerged hurriedly from under the table and offered my congratulations to Captain Williams, who was singing at the top of his voice with a look of ecstasy suffusing his small Welsh face. General Holdenhurst was beaming. Sheldrake was trying to conceal his disappointment at his team's failure and his deeply felt resentment of what he saw as the general's act of injustice.

We were ushered by a group of personable young captains to the places we had been allotted for the presentation. Shelduck and I were at opposite ends of the second bench. Captain Williams, in the middle of our bench, craned forward to give me the leeks up sign.

General Holdenhurst made the speech of congratulation, Lady Holdenhurst presented the cup to the colonel of the Sharpshooters. Not being a connoisseur of military protocol I was unaware that the entire audience would rise for the moment of presentation. This would have mattered less had I not been sitting at one end of a bench from which everyone else suddenly got up, with the result that it sank violently to the ground under my weight, while the other end, in the manner of a medieval siege instrument, propelled Shelduck's handbag in a high arc almost as far as the band, who were at that moment arranging their music for yet another selection from *Iolanthe*.

The moment was not lost on the crowd. There was an appreciative good-natured cheer. General Holdenhurst, looking round and taking in the situation in a flash, announced into the microphone 'Most promising newcomer – J.R. Hartley.' I went bright red, the crowd applauded, the band broke into the selection from *Iolanthe*, and we went off to lunch in the officers' mess at Larkhill, just down the road.

I shan't dwell on the hospitality at Larkhill, which was handsome and attentive. Some of the Sharpshooters got a little out of control and became too nationalistic for my taste, but I was satisfied, watching the scene, that a standard of meal-taking was being set among the hierarchy that would allow ample room for quality reductions down the military ladder without having to resort to lentil dunking.

Then it was back to the river by helicopter. We landed on the lunch table. Standing nearby, erect against the winnowing blades, stood the general's driver. He saluted. 'Your fishing things are laid out in the Saracen, sir. And they've put through the fishing licence, to run from today, as you instructed, sir.'

The general saw my look of impressed astonishment.

'Mustn't leave your flank exposed,' he said. Then he suggested that I take the lower beat this afternoon, and with that he headed off towards the waiting Saracen, accompanied by the driver.

As I warily approached the river I saw fish moving in the two pools immediately below the bridge. I took a view that a Black Gnat might be the answer, and indeed it was. I hooked a fish close by the opposite bank and though he gave me some anxious moments in the weed, I brought him successfully to the net, a brown trout of about a pound. I repeated the experience in the next pool, another brownie coming for my Black Gnat almost immediately. There were one or two grayling moving in the centre of the stream but I had my eye open for the telltale movement near the banks, which tended to be feeding trout.

General Holdenhurst had emerged again from the Saracen in his fishing mufti. He called out a breezy greeting as he passed behind me, moving upstream, and congratulated me on my success. What a colossus he was! The Russian military machine would ping backwards from him like a pea fired from a peashooter against a suit of armour.

I was fishing with great content. The setting was pleasing, the weather agreeable, the sport challenging but full of promise. I was rehearsing my account of the day's excitements for the bursar. I knew he'd dredge up some anecdote from the ranges at Lulworth to cap my story, but I suppose that's how a balance sheet gets balanced.

Then I saw a car stopping almost opposite me, where the road is separated from the river by only a short grass descent. The driver reversed into the access to a private garage, so that the bonnet was pointing straight towards me. As he got out and began to hurry to the footbridge to come over to my side, I saw he was a special constable. I also saw the military presence stirring discreetly in the vicinity of his car.

There was a whiff of betrayal about the way he approached with such purpose. Not Sheldrake, surely, trying to get back at the general?

'Good afternoon, sir,' he said. 'Could I trouble you for your game fishing licence?'

I made some indeterminate noises. He seemed to relish my obvious guilt. 'I'm afraid it slipped my mind,' I said.

'Well, we'll have to unslip it, won't we, sir?' he said. He produced a pencil and pad from his tunic pocket. Then, in an affected display of recognition that would have done no credit even to the Combermere school play, he said, 'Don't I know you, sir? It's General Holdenhurst, isn't it?'

Shame on you, Sheldrake.

I didn't exactly not reply, but I didn't communicate the true position. Fortunately I didn't have to; because the constable's car suddenly began to move towards us and with a brisk hop, skip and a jump down the grassy incline landed upside down in the river with a tremendous splash. I saw General Holdenhurst's driver standing where the car had been parked. The general himself was hurrying down the bank towards us.

'That's my car,' the constable gasped.

'It's not in a very good place,' I said.

'No,' he said, 'I mean it's my car. It's not a police car.'

'Well,' I suggested facetiously, 'you may have a grayling down the back seat.'

He bridled.

'If you don't watch it,' he said, 'you may have a grayling *up* the back seat.'

General Holdenhurst closed in.

'Don't you speak to my guest like that,' he ordered, 'and get that car out of the river at once.'

The constable seemed emotionally strangled.

'Sod off, you,' he said.

General Holdenhurst regarded him evenly.

'If you don't both apologise and get that car out of the river before I count twenty, I shall call the police.'

This was too much.

'I am the police,' he shouted. 'You stupid bastard.'

'One,' said General Holdenhurst.

'Don't you one me,' the constable rasped.

'Two,' said General Holdenhurst.

The confrontation must have ended in physical violence had not the constable been distracted by a group of soldiers gathering to retrieve his car. The Saracen had backed down the road with a towrope attached. The soldiers were trying to attach it to the back bumper.

'Oh no,' the constable howled, 'they'll pull off that bumper.'

He broke away and ran towards the bridge. As he crossed it and ran frantically back down the road towards the soldiers, the Saracen moved forward and to a tremendous roar of laughter the bumper danced unaccompanied up the bank.

General Holdenhurst looked on with approval.

'Treachery, thy name is Sheldrake,' I said.

I could see General Holdenhurst's mental control systems ranging through Quotations, Shakespeare, Treachery, for the illustration of. The *Julius Caesar* cogs whirred into place.

'See what a rent', he said, 'the envious Casca paid.'

Should I or shouldn't I correct him?

'Made,' I murmured.

On the way home, settled in the car, I addressed the back of the driver's head.

'I think we had a stroke of luck with the constable's handbrake,' I said.

'Thank you, sir,' he replied, in a perfect economy of explanation.

We turned into the school gates. My car was up by the front

door. Could I get away without being seen by the bursar?

We stopped. The driver opened the door.

'Could you possibly put my things in that car,' I said.

I was just getting into the driver's seat, ready to go home, when I saw the bursar coming down the front steps. He had his I'm-going-to-make-a-joke face on.

'Well, you've really done it,' he called out. 'Have you heard? It's Bay of Pigs squared. They're on their way.'

'Let 'em come,' I said, beginning to wind up my window. 'They're wasting their time.'

9
Storm Warning

The Cassley runs down to join the Oykel through a theatrical Sutherland glen. Centre stalls sits Glencassley Castle, a nineteenth-century brewer's creation, not over-large, certainly not over-attractive, but with all the confidence of the eccentric squire. Behind the house the land rises to secure the glen along one side, while to the front the hills, pushed back by the broad turn of the river, manage to combine the role of both boundary and view, accommodating to perfection the brewer's aesthetic and proprietorial requirement. Even the woodland that begins to clothe the river down below the house looks part of the legacy of centuries, none of your grow-by-night conifers splurged like estate paint across the fell. The river here is on its best behaviour, approaching in sensible runs between easy banks, Long Pool, Castle Pool, perhaps with half an eye to the sporting convenience of the quality.

Its earlier descent is more dramatic. It moves with no great sense of purpose across the open moorland that merges the commanding distance with Glencassley proper, until it meets the falls. Over the first step it writhes briefly in a trough of rock where poachers have the nerve and knack to hoist out salmon; then plunges gloriously down to sprawl in side eddies before gathering itself to run between steep wooded banks through bouldered pools; then in a left-handed sweep, on one side holding back the fell, it rides past tussocked heather to the Wash Pool turn. In a dry spell you can ford the river there and Henry once had a salmon glance against his waders as it thrust up the narrow channel on the gravel bend; and sometimes when the fish are moving and the water's up, you see them on the long open stretch below the Wash Pool breaking the surface at even intervals, as if some traffic controller were giving them their clearance to approach.

A road comes up from Rosehall to the head of the glen, following the line of the river as far as the Wash Pool bend. At the Rosehall end is the Achness Hotel, where anglers stay to fish the Cassley down from the lower falls. Henry and Lawrence were putting up there, with their wives to come up the following week, while Helen and I were housed in a cottage up the glen, fifty yards below the road, two up, two down, with its adjoining cow-byre thankfully disused. Barbara had elected not to come and had gone off with a group of school friends in pursuit of something more exciting, mistaking the Continent for the exotic.

That first day Henry had a six-pound salmon in the morning, which took his Green Highlander close under the bank two hundred yards below the Wash Pool on the castle side. I lost quite a good fish a little further up; Lawrence had a morning of excited anticipation but no more. Helen had decided to defer her efforts until after lunch and took the car off down the glen to do some shopping for our stay. At lunch time, before changing banks for the afternoon's efforts, we had a picnic outside the cottage, pitched against the shelter of the cow-byre wall. The salad niçoise was not the only *tour de force*. Henry and Lawrence got involved in a juggling display, Henry with three cucumbers, Lawrence with three apples, which Helen accurately predicted would end in tears. Becoming over confident, they tried to make an exchange, and an off-course cucumber knocked a glass of beer into the summer pudding.

After lunch Helen dismissed our rather half-hearted offers to assist and took the remnants of the meal inside. Lawrence tipped his hat forward over his eyes and stretched out on the grass. Henry got into one of his diatribes – this time on left- and right-handed scripts – which he preferred to think of as conversation, although Lawrence's only contribution was an intermittent assurance that he was still awake. I smoked my pipe and looked on complacently, reflecting what a thing it was to be happy in the minutiae of tested friendship. Thirty years had gone by since that day on the Coln when I'd seen the others crossed by the passing shadow and had been afraid it was a warning; and after thirty years I could surely count myself a failed Cassandra. Yet in that time the three of us had changed so similarly and so gradually that it was as if we had never changed at all, and here we were in a mere extension of those Oxford days.

Although we still snatched a day's fishing together when we could, these holidays were a special luxury because we could indulge ourselves at leisure as friends and anglers and, I dare say, bores. Our wives condoned it all without quite relinquishing the reins, but in the main they understood the bond of shared enthusiasms. Helen was the only one of the three to fish herself, but fortunately for the others she had inherited from her mother the habit of reproof when we fell into talking too much 'shop'. And whereas her mother's preferred method was to leave the room in protest, Helen opted for the less oblique approach and told us, simply, to shut up.

We took the car back to the Wash Pool and stopped to talk there to two anglers from the castle before we went our separate ways. Lawrence pressed me to try his new fibreglass rod, which I found too soft compared to my faithful old split cane and told him so. I knew that he had confided to Henry that he didn't like it much himself, but he wasn't going to waste the opportunity of calling me a diehard. I reminded him he'd done that twenty years ago when I denounced his new steel rod for the heavy, floppy brute it was, made from an old tank aerial, which some of us called army surplus but which seemed to Lawrence, until it rusted, progress.

We saw some fish that flattered us by moving near the fly, but nothing took. I tried fishing below the overhang of a deeply submerged rock, which I had been told by our friends from the castle was a place where salmon sometimes lay. Time and again I let the fly sink slowly down and coursed it past the ledge, then remembered how I'd laughed at Mrs Charlton's efforts at the Inverpolly sea pool. My own performance now wasn't much more artful and probably even less likely to succeed.

About half past four the afternoon grew sultry. Helen had given up and was sitting watching near the car. The river was lifeless; I reeled in and walked back to the road to join her. My morale, for some reason, had been in serious decline. I was conscious of tensions that tell me there is thunder in the offing. The wind had dropped to nothing and I suspected Nature had something nasty up her sleeve. It's when you're reminded of the enormous advantages she has in size that you're wise to give the maximum attention to your 'p's an 'q's.

'Thunder about,' I said to Helen.

'Yes,' she said, 'I think I'll go back to the cottage.' I told her to go on. I'd wait there for the others.

I sat down on the grass and stretched out my legs. Henry was about a hundred yards up to my left, casting with his marvellous easy rhythm; he was as tenacious an angler as you could find, always full of advice if you needed it, yet the first to support Walton's celebrated dictum: 'Angling is like mathematics, that it can never be fully learnt.' He was also a considerable ornithologist, with that capacity for almost intuitive observation that sets the practised countryman apart. Aware that I was watching him, he waved and pointed to two greenshanks, and I waved back to show that I had seen them too.

Then, for some reason, I was beset with a feeling of menace, irrational but very strong, as if too keen an awareness of the pleasures of our friendship had somehow compromised its permanence. It was no more than echoing the earlier alarms – when I'd seen Henry and Lawrence in shadow on the Coln, or when I'd looked down on the poacher's face beside the Shimna; and, as the others intermittently reminded me, those premonitions so far hadn't added up to much. I should have been glad to agree. What's more, I should have rejected the charge that I was superstitious, just as I should have claimed that I could rationalise the paranormal, believing that all that disquieting evidence was accounted for by a flaw in the process of perception rather than an upending of the natural law.

I wrote a note for Henry and Lawrence to say that I'd walked back and we'd see them both for supper. I put it under one of the windscreen wipers of the car, picked up my things and set off along the road. Far ahead of me, beyond the head of the glen, the sky was black and I could see occasional flashes of forked lightning stabbing at the hills. The rumble of thunder was safely in the distance. It looked as if Glencassley itself was going to miss the storm.

My unsettled state of mind persisted. Helen, quick to sense it, asked me what was wrong. My explanation sounded silly but I was glad to get it off my chest. 'I shouldn't worry,' she said, 'thunder always upsets you.'

When the others arrived for supper, Helen told them, although I had asked her not to, that I was out of sorts. 'Do perk him up,' she said.

Lawrence laughed. 'Do you think it might be an attack of Henrycaughtmoresalmonitis?'

'How typical,' I called out, overhearing him. 'My two best friends are a doctor and a farmer, and in my hour of travail the one who gives the diagnosis is the farmer.'

It was a congenial evening and, assisted perhaps by a glass or two of wine, my anxieties to some extent receded. So much so that I asked the others, when they said they must be getting back to the hotel, to give me a lift as far as the Wash Pool and I'd have a cast or two for a sea trout.

They seemed cheered by the suggestion. Helen said she'd be going to bed. She'd leave the downstairs light on. I got down my rod and went to put on my waders. When I came back Henry and Lawrence were saying their goodnights.

Henry pulled up at the nearest point to the river to let me out of the car. We had a brief discussion about flies and the most likely pools, then I watched them drive off down the glen, the shaft of the headlights rising and ducking with the undulations of the road.

I walked about five hundred yards up from the Wash Pool bend and then started fishing down. There was some moon, possibly a little too much for sea trout purposes, but my principal concern was not a full bag of fish but a chance to settle myself down.

I was using a floating line with a nine-foot leader with a single dropper, casting across the stream and allowing the flies to work round in the current. At the tail of the second pool a fish took me with a thump, hurtling backwards and forwards and jumping two or three times before I brought him to the net. He was a sea trout of perhaps a pound and a half. I knelt on the bank with my back to the river, detached the hook, killed my fish, and inspected the flies by the light of my pencil torch. They seemed not too bedraggled, so holding them with an extended left arm and with my rod in my right hand, I stood up to turn and go down

towards the next pool. As I did so, I saw someone was watching me.

He was standing about forty yards away, too far to distinguish much, if anything, about his appearance except that from his build and his clothes he was a man. I looked at him with some misgivings. Had he been one of the castle party he'd have surely either left me undisturbed or called out a greeting as he passed. Besides, watching a fisherman in broad daylight was one thing, standing there gazing at him in the dark was decidedly another. We had been told, too, by one of the fishermen from the castle that a deer-poaching gang had been operating in the glen and these were not only rough customers but armed. I wasn't going to take any risks; I had no desire to be on my way to Germany on the morrow as part of a cargo of venison. On the other hand I didn't want to take ignominiously to my heels and find that it had been a harmless onlooker from the castle all along. My idea therefore was gradually to get away from him without being too obvious about it.

I walked to the bank and waded in a couple of yards, then started to move steadily but not over-anxiously downstream, even casting regularly to give an impression of normality. The river seemed to afford me some protection, and I decided to keep wading until I got away from him. At the tail of the next pool I came back towards the bank and looked to see if he had followed me.

I saw him almost at once. He had moved down level with me, about the same distance into the heather. He was motionless, watching. There was a malevolence about his stillness.

I re-entered the water. I was frightened now, of what I didn't know, but my imagination began to race. I told myself to keep calm. There was a good distance between us and if I could get safely down river another hundred and fifty yards, I could probably wade across to the other side.

My progress downstream was now of floundering haste. I dispensed with any show of casting and kept turning to see if he was following. He seemed to have stayed where he was; I couldn't hear any sound of movement. I was just thinking I'd got clear when I saw him again, just as before, level with me, motionless, watching. It was like some terrifying game of Grandmother's Footsteps.

I panicked. My one instinct was to get back to Helen. It was still about two hundred and fifty yards even to get to the road, and that involved crossing the narrow footbridge over the burn that joined the river at the Wash Pool. The night around me seemed cavernous and unprotecting. There was nothing for it, I must run. I didn't look behind me, I expected at any moment to see him appear between me and the bridge and cut off my line of escape. He didn't. I got there first. I staggered on to the double planks, clung to the handrail and looked back, gasping. There was no sign or sound of him. I peered in the direction of where I'd last seen him. Nothing. I dared to think that now he'd frightened me off he'd gone to get on with whatever he was there to do. As I crossed the bridge, the shock of my experience came suddenly home to me. My legs were shaky, so I rested for a few moments, head down, breathing deeply. Then I summoned my resources to get back to the cottage; and as I started up the short rise from the bridge, I saw him again. He was standing in front of me, just on the other side of the road, closer now, still watching.

The next few minutes were of total nightmare. I ran blindly to my left, scrambled across some boggy ground, and somehow got up on to the road. I remember wondering what chance there was of seeing a car coming. None came. Gradually I began to lose speed, moving almost mechanically, the felt soles of my waders thudding on the road. I wasn't now trying to get away because in my mind I was already caught, and whatever was going to happen to me I expected to happen at any moment. More strongly than anything else I felt a sense of unfairness, both to myself and to Helen and my daughter. Yet still nothing happened, and when my physical reserves were all but drained, there was the cottage, the light spilling from the sitting-room window. I ran for it as I'd never run before, in desperation and then suddenly in hope. I reached the front door and threw aside my rod so as not to lose a second getting inside. As I looked to my left towards the cow-byre a man – the man – was standing looking at me, not ten yards away. In the light from the window I saw him properly for the first time. His clothes were drenched and clinging to him. I froze with terror. It was the drowned poacher from the Shimna and on his face was the stare of troubled death.

Helen rescued me from the hall and helped me upstairs to our bedroom. I was evidently in a state of severe shock. She said she'd better go and get Henry from the hotel, since there was no telephone in the cottage; but my reaction was of such panic that she decided she couldn't leave me on my own.

My account of what had happened alarmed her less in its detail or in any threat it might imply to her than for the emotional damage it had clearly done to me. She didn't, deep down, believe my story but she had no choice but to accept that it had – for whatever reason – implanted itself on my consciousness. Her own interpretation, she told me later, was that I had indeed seen a man by the river, quite likely one of the poachers, the shock of whose appearance had triggered the subsequent images. I had been, on my own admission, in rather a troubled frame of mind and seeing the man would have been a frightening enough experience in any circumstances. For myself, I honestly don't know. I can only wonder if these rationally unexplainable phenomena should be so summarily dismissed.

Cleverly, Helen didn't try to persuade me in the hours that

followed that I had imagined it all. Her first thought was to diminish its impact, to suggest that if it were some sort of a warning, it was benign. With the coming of daylight I was more manageable, the very fact that I had escaped began to lift me a little. I'd dealt unsuccessfully in premonitions before, and I was wary of claiming that the manifestation of the poacher was trying to tell me something. What is not in dispute, however, is that as a result of it I was not in a fit physical condition to go out fishing the following day and Helen felt she should stay with me. That very possibly saved our lives.

When Henry and Lawrence arrived to pick us up, I told them I was not well enough to go with them. I had made Helen promise not to mention the poacher. I told them about the mystery man on the river bank, and they said they would report it to the police. I could see that Henry was concerned about me and that he wanted to question me further, to find out if I was keeping something back. He gave me some professional instructions and said he'd see me later. At that moment I all but confided in him and begged him to treat the apparition as a warning. I'm sure that he would have gently shrugged it off. Then he and Lawrence drove back down the glen to fish.

What happened later is on public record. At about four o'clock that afternoon there was a phenomenal storm. The sides of the glen were soon awash with water coursing down the swollen burns. The river burst its banks below us in the glen; though our little house was safe, water poured through the hall in Glencassley Castle. One of the guests there, taking shelter in a cottage, saw the cottage cat incandescent with electricity. It survived, to have its experience recounted in the local paper and to enjoy a well-deserved celebrity thereafter as 'the electric cat'.

The flood was swift and terrifying. Henry and Lawrence

independently – and sensibly – made for high ground rather than going down to the car. I'm not sure that Helen and I would have done the same. The car was swept away. This we knew for an hour before the news reached us that Henry and Lawrence were safe. It was the worst hour of my life. I was tortured, fearing them drowned, that this time they would have heeded my premonition. In fact, in talking to them later, they convinced me that they would have disregarded it. In the light of what afterwards transpired, I had to conclude that the premonition – if such it was – was intended for Helen and myself.

There was a curious and salutary sequel. A body of a man who appeared to have died by drowning was found two days later washed up in the wood below the castle. No local people were missing and the body was never formally identified. I read in due course that the pathologist's report mentioned bruising on the face and found it difficult to reconcile the probable time of death with drowning in the Glencassley flood. To me the inference was shockingly obvious, but I didn't dare come forward with my idea of the solution. As it was, I felt suddenly and eerily liberated from the presentiments that had haunted me all those years. It was as if the Shimna poacher had expiated the old forebodings and given us safe conduct into an untroubled future. We were borne (*pace* the conclusion of *The Great Gatsby*) no longer ceaselessly into the past nor, better still, peacelessly into the cast.

Meanwhile I fish on, sometimes, invited by kind friends, in new locations. More to remember, more to recount. At Combermere, as we move into the Seventies, we groom the little Ellinghams and Charltons and Rendlesham-Bullers for a world that is supposed to have disappeared but still seems in many ways surprisingly the same. And, who knows, we may become a literary Mecca. The bursar, miffed by the publisher's acceptance of this slight memoir, is writing his autobiography. Ever competitive, he is entitling it *All the Way to the Bank.*